ALCOHOL AND DRUGS

The Scottish Experience

EDITED BY

Martin Plant, Bruce Ritson
and Roy Robertson

Edinburgh University Press

© Edinburgh University Press, 1992

Edinburgh University Press
22 George Square, Edinburgh

Typeset in New Century Schoolbook
by Combined Arts, Edinburgh,
and printed in Great Britain
by the Alden Press, Osney Mead, Oxford

A CIP record for this book is available from the British Library

ISBN 0 7486 0377 8

CONTENTS

PART III SERVICE PROVISION

CONTRIBUTORS

PHILIP P. AITKEN Formerly Advertising Research Unit, Department of Marketing, University of Strathclyde

DOUGLAS ALLSOP Scottish Council on Alcohol, Glasgow

GELLISSE BAGNALL Alcohol Research Group, Department of Psychiatry, University of Edinburgh

STEVE BALDWIN Neighbourhood Evaluations, Edinburgh

KEN BARRIE Alcohol Studies Centre, Paisley College, Paisley

RAY BRETTLE Infectious Diseases Unit, City Hospital, Edinburgh

PETER W. BRUNT Gastrointestinal and Liver Service, Aberdeen Royal Infirmary, Aberdeen

JONATHAN CHICK Alcohol Problems Clinic, Royal Edinburgh Hospital, Edinburgh

NIALL COGGANS Addictions Research Group, Department of Psychology, University of Strathclyde

JOHN B. DAVIES Addiction Research Group, Department of Psychology, University of Strathclyde

JOHN DUFFY Alcohol Research Group, Department of Psychiatry, University of Edinburgh

JAMES DUNBAR University Department of Forensic Medicine, Royal Infirmary, Dundee

JOHN EMSLIE Communicable Diseases (Scotland) Unit, Ruchill Hospital, Glasgow

DAVID GOLDBERG Communicable Diseases (Scotland) Unit, Ruchill Hospital, Glasgow

JUDY GREENWOOD Community Drug Problems Service, Royal Edinburgh Hospital, Edinburgh

MARY HARTNOLL Department of Social Work, Aberdeen

GERARD B. HASTINGS Advertising Research Unit, Department of Marketing, University of Strathclyde

DERMOT KENNEDY Department of Infectious and Tropical Medicine, Ruchill Hospital, Glasgow

RUTH MORGAN THOMAS Alcohol Research Group, Department of Psychiatry, University of Edinburgh

ALASDAIR MURRAY Tayside Area Clinical Psychology Department, Royal Dundee Liff Hospital, Dundee

DANIEL PATON Faculty of Engineering, Birmingham Polytechnic, Birmingham

JOHN PEARCE HM Prison, Saughton, Edinburgh

MARTIN PLANT Alcohol Research Group, Department of Psychiatry, University of Edinburgh

MOIRA PLANT Alcohol Research Group, Department of Psychiatry, University of Edinburgh

BRUCE RITSON Alcohol Problems Clinic, Royal Edinburgh Hospital, Edinburgh

ROY ROBERTSON Edinburgh Drug Addiction Study, Muirhouse Medical Group, Muirhouse, Edinburgh

WILLY SLAVIN Scottish Drugs Forum, Glasgow

FOREWORD

It was Winston Churchill who once said that he had 'taken more out of alcohol than alcohol has taken out of me'. This pithy observation underlines the colossal ambivalence about alcohol consumption – and perhaps to a lesser extent about some other addictive drugs – which characterises most societies today. If we are honest we drink alcohol because we like it – and those who use other addictive drugs, more or less harmful, would say the same thing. The pragmatic answer lies in 'control' – both at a social level and at an individual level. But understanding the scientific, cultural and ethical foundations of control, the causes and consequences of 'loss of control' and how the positive elements of human nature can be stimulated and harnessed for good, reflects many, as yet, unanswered questions.

Scotland is proud to be host to the 1992 International Congresss on Alcohol and Drug Dependence. This country is not without its own enormous problems of alcohol abuse, a high coronary heart disease mortality partially linked to smoking, and an unenviable picture of illicit drugs and an associated AIDS problem. It also has a reputation for vigorous, practical and effective research in many areas of alcohol and drug misuse and for its programmes of tackling the problems within society. The Professional Advisory Committee of the Scottish Council on Alcohol felt that it would be most appropriate to mark the Congress's time in Glasgow if much of this expertise could be brought together in a readable and informative form, as it has never thus far appeared. It asked three very distinguished workers in the field, Dr Martin Plant, Dr Bruce Ritson and Dr Roy Robertson, to invite, collate and edit contributions from Scotland, about Scotland and in Scotland. The resulting compilation is stimulating and, we trust, a fitting tribute to all those from many parts of the world who are working towards a solution to drug-related problems and whom Scotland is warmly welcoming to its shores this summer.

PETER W. BRUNT
Chairman
Professional Advisory Committee on Alcohol
Scottish Council on Alcohol
1982–91

PREFACE

The occasion of the thirty-sixth International Congress on Alcohol and Drug Dependence in Glasgow during August 1992 provided the impetus to the production of this multi-author book. The following chapters offer a selection of reviews. Each of these reflects, to at least a degree, issues relating to psychoactive drug use and misuse in Scotland and elsewhere. All of the contributors to this volume are either based in Scotland or at least have a strong Scottish connection. The editors have attempted to compile a volume which, though by no means comprehensive, provides a useful sample of past and current concerns in the 'addictions field' in Scotland. It is emphasised that, while some of the following chapters relate to specifically Scottish issues or Scottish research, the majority relate to issues of worldwide concern. Scotland is, in some respects, distinctive and particularly so in relation to the pattern of service responses to alcohol and other drug problems. Even so, most of the topics reviewed in this book are themes which concern people in many countries where alcohol and other forms of drug misuse pose serious problems.

For the purposes of this book contributions have been divided into three sections. Although this division has been somewhat arbitrary, it is not wholly unsatisfactory. Part I presents a general account of the recent epidemiology of alcohol, tobacco and illicit drug use in Scotland, and a historical overview of the use of alcohol and illicit drugs. Other chapters relate to alcohol and health; alcohol, drugs, tobacco and pregnancy, alcohol, drugs and sexual behaviour; AIDS in Scotland and clinical aspects of HIV/AIDS among alcohol and drug users.

Part II – PREVENTION AND CONTROLS – includes critical reviews of the effectiveness of alcohol and drug education. In addition, other contributors discuss the role of advertising in relation to youthful drinking, the impact of Scottish liquor licensing changes, drinking and driving, alcohol and young offenders and minimal intervention with problem drinkers.

Part III – SERVICE PROVISION – begins with a description of voluntary services in Scotland for alcohol and drug problems. In addition reviews are presented of health and social work services for problem drinkers and drug users, primary care for problem drug users, alcohol and drug problems in prison, the problems involved in evaluating programmes and services and professional training.

It is hoped that this collection of reviews will give an introductory account of 'the Scottish scene'. It is also hoped that the material presented will contribute to a better understanding of the form of and responses to the misuse of legal and illicit drugs.

Martin Plant
Bruce Ritson
Roy Robertson

ACKNOWLEDGEMENTS

The editors would like to thank the contributors to this book for compressing their extensive knowledge and experience into extremely short chapters. This book owes its compilation to the organizers of the 36th International Congress on Alcohol and Drug Dependence in Glasgow during August 1992. They are thanked for their inspiration and support. This manuscript was processed with remarkable speed, efficiency, tolerance and good humour by Mrs Joyce Greig, Mrs Sheila MacLennan and Mrs Janis Nichol, of the Alcohol Research Group, University of Edinburgh. Figures were produced by the Medical Illustrations Department, University of Edinburgh. The production of this book was supported by the Scottish Office.

PART I

THE BACKGROUND

1. Alcohol, tobacco and illicit drug use in Scotland

MARTIN PLANT

Scotland and England have shared a common crown since 1603 and have had a common parliament since 1707. Scotland is an integral part of the United Kingdom (England, Scotland, Wales and Northern Ireland) but retains a distinctive national identity and traditions. Scotland has considerable independence in relation to health and social issues. The population of Scotland is approximately 5,000,000, while the rest of the United Kingdom contains a further 51,000,000 people.

There has long been a popular belief in the United Kingdom that the Scots are more likely than the English or the Welsh, but not necessarily the Irish, to drink heavily. (In fact, alcohol consumption levels in Northern Ireland are generally lower than they are in Britain (Wilson 1980; Brewers' Society 1991).) Moreover, Scotland has traditionally experienced more than its share of the UK's social problems, particularly unemployment. The historical background of alcohol use and misuse in Scotland is elaborated in the next chapter. The misuse of alcohol, tobacco and illicit drugs is firmly established as a major problem in Scotland. This chapter attempts to provide a selective review of some of the recent research into the use and misuse of these substances.

ALCOHOL

Alcohol, as noted in a recent report, is the favourite drug not only of the Scots but of the British in general (Royal College of Psychiatrists 1986). Over ninety per cent of adult Scots drink alcohol at least occasionally, and recent studies have indicated that very few teenagers in Scotland have not at least tasted alcoholic drinks (Plant, Peck and Samuel 1985; Bagnall 1991; Plant and Foster 1991). Several surveys of Scottish drinking habits have been conducted in recent years. These have generally failed to confirm the belief that the Scots drink more than do their English counterparts (e.g. Dight 1976; Foster, Wilmot and Dobbs 1990).

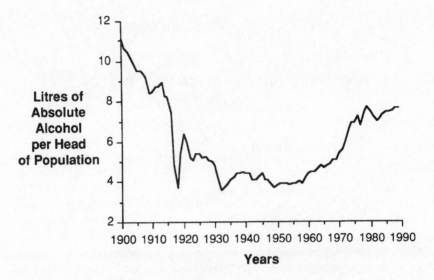

Figure 1.1 Per capita alcohol consumption in the United Kingdom (1900–89)
(Source: Thurman 1991)

In addition, regional variations of 'alcohol problems' such as alcohol
dependence admissions to hospitals, though evident within Britain,
appear relatively modest (Crawford et al. 1984; Latcham et al. 1984;
Crawford and Plant 1986). There are no separate details of per capita
alcohol consumption in Scotland. Even so, information is available for
the UK as a whole. Figure 1.1 indicates the pattern of consumption in
the UK over the period 1900–89.

As the figure shows, alcohol consumption fell sharply during the first
three decades of this century, but has risen steadily since the end of the
Second World War. Per capita consumption reached a postwar peak in
1979. The UK is not remarkable in its alcohol consumption. During 1989,
per capita alcohol consumption in the UK was 7.3 litres, much lower than
in countries such as France (13.2 litres) and similar to that in the USA
(7.7 litres) or Canada (7.8 litres) (Brewers' Society 1991).

The fluctuations in alcohol consumption shown in Figure 1.1 have
been accompanied by considerable changes in the levels of alcohol-related problems. Predictably these fell during times of declining consumption but have risen markedly in association with the postwar increase
in per capita consumption (Sales et al. 1989). As shown by Figure 1.1
alcohol consumption has been at a slightly *lower* level in recent years
than it was in 1979. This has been reflected by a fall or levelling out in
different types of alcohol problems. Even so, these persist at a relatively
high level and appear to be a chronic feature of the national scene.
Concern about the extent of alcohol misuse led to a liberalisation of

liquor licensing laws in 1976. This is discussed by John Duffy in Chapter 11. As in many other countries, alcohol misuse is far more extensive than the misuse of illicit drugs. Even though Scotch whisky is the nation's most famous export, the Scots, like other northern Europeans, are distinctly ambivalent about the role of alcohol. The misuse of alcohol is associated with a wide range of public order, health and social problems in Scotland (Scottish Health Education Co-ordinating Committee 1985).

Recent studies have shown that young Scots are inclined to drink less frequently, but more heavily on specific occasions, than do their English counterparts (e.g. Plant and Foster 1991). In spite of this, available evidence suggests that UK drinking habits are, or have been, relatively uniform with only marginal differences being evident between regions.

As in other countries, the heavy consumption of alcohol is often associated with tobacco use and the use of illicit drugs. Evidence from Scotland suggests that young people who drink heavily are indeed particularly likely to smoke or to use illicit drugs. Moreover, early heavy drinking is associated with subsequent illicit drug use but does not appear to predict the later development of alcohol problems (Plant, Peck and Samuel 1985, Bagnall 1991).

TOBACCO

Scotland has the unenviable reputation of having the world's highest rate of mortality from coronary heart disease. There is no doubt that a major factor behind this mortality is cigarette smoking and poor diet. Tobacco is responsible for far more health damage than are all of the other psychoactive drugs combined (Royal College of Physicians 1977, 1986).

Scots have consistently been more inclined to smoke than have the English. This tendency persists, but there has been an encouraging decline in the overall level of smoking, both in Scotland and elsewhere in the UK.

The Royal College of Physicians (1977) reported that, even when male cigarette smoking was declining, females in Britain continued to smoke more between 1950 and 1976. Recently, the proportion of smokers among both males and females has decreased in Britain as a whole. Leck et al. (1981) reported that the proportion of adults who smoked had dropped to thirty-one per cent in 1984. Between 1972 and 1982 the proportion of adult females who smoked declined from forty-two to thirty-three per cent. Foster, Wilmot and Dobbs (1990) have concluded that between 1972 and 1988 the prevalence of cigarette smoking fell among all age groups surveyed in Britain. The same authors concluded that the prevalence of cigarette smoking in 1988 was higher in Scotland (thirty-seven per cent) than elsewhere in Britain. Smoking was least prevalent in Southern England (twenty-eight to twenty-nine per cent) and highest in the North

of England (thirty-six per cent) where the prevalence almost equalled
that in Scotland. It must be noted that in 1974 the prevalence of smoking
in Scotland had been much higher, at forty-eight per cent, than it was
in 1988. Even so smoking had declined less in Scotland over this period
than it had elsewhere in Britain. The variations in smoking habits
evident in different areas of Britain certainly reflect a variety of factors,
such as socioeconomic status. The latter is important because smoking
is markedly more popular among those in lower socioeconomic positions
than among 'upscale' individuals.

The scale of tobacco-related mortality continues to be massive. The
Royal College of Physicians (1986) reported that tobacco is implicated
in fifteen to twenty per cent of British deaths. Scotland's mortality has
certainly been more severely influenced by smoking than has that in
areas of Britain in which a lower proportion of the population smoke. In
1988 over 4,000 people in Scotland died from cancers of the bronchus,
trachea or lung. In the same year over 20,000 people in Scotland died of
heart disease. Tobacco smoking is a major contributor to such deaths
(Registrar General Scotland 1989).

ILLICIT DRUGS

It is alleged that the first use of an opiate drug by hypodermic syringe
occurred, under medical advice, in Edinburgh. The use of opium was
widespread throughout Britain during the eighteenth and nineteenth
centuries (Berridge and Edwards 1981).

Only relatively low levels of opiate or other illicit drug use were
reported either in Scotland or elsewhere in Britain during the first half
of the twentieth century (Edwards and Busch 1981; Royal College of
Psychiatrists 1987; Plant 1987; Plant and Plant 1992). This situation
was transformed during the 1960s with the development of 'the drug
scene' in Britain. Illicit drug use has been evident all over the United
Kingdom during the past thirty years. 'Official indicators' such as Home
Office records of drug convictions and 'addict notifications' indicate that
the trends in drug misuse have been steadily, and sometimes sharply,
upwards (Scottish Health Education Group 1986; MacGregor 1989;
Berridge 1990). During the 1960s and 1970s Scotland appeared to be
rather less affected by the spread of illicit drugs than was England. More
recently drug use and misuse in Scotland appear to have at least
equalled the English rates. Between 1975 and 1990 the number of
'notified addicts' in Scotland rose from fifty-eight to 1,184. The numbers
of persons cautioned and convicted for drug offences rose from approximately 500 in 1975 to 2,626 in 1988 (Home Office 1990, 1991; Scottish
Office 1991). During 1979 / 80, a survey of 1,036 fifteen- and sixteen-
year-olds in the Lothian Region indicated that approximately ten per
cent had used illicit drugs or other non-prescribed substances, mainly

cannabis or glues and solvents. Four years later, a third of this study group had used such drugs. A national survey conducted during 1982 indicated that the level of self-reported drug use among fifteen to twenty-one-year-olds in Scotland was higher than that in the Midlands or the north of England (NOP Market Research Ltd 1982). The British Crime Survey further indicated that nineteen per cent of those aged between twenty and twenty-four in Scotland had used cannabis (Chambers and Tombs 1984; Mott 1989).

Coggans et al. (1989) concluded that almost twenty-three per cent of a sample of Scottish teenagers had used illicit drugs. Such surveys suggest that the overall pattern of Scottish drug use is similar to that in England. One striking difference has, however, emerged which is of enormous importance. During the early 1980s it became evident that very high levels of HIV infection had become established amongst young intravenous drug users in Edinburgh and Dundee (Robertson 1987; Strang and Stimson 1990; Morrison and Plant 1990; Morrison 1991). In Edinburgh such infection was recorded among over half of one group of intravenous drug users tested and in Dundee the corresponding proportion was a third. At the end of 1990, 945 out of 1,840 people in Scotland who were recorded as HIV seropositive were intravenous drug users. Over sixty per cent of these were recorded in Edinburgh, Dundee and Glasgow. In contrast only one in seven of HIV seropositive people in the UK as a whole were intravenous drug users (ANSWER 1991). HIV infection has been transmitted perinatally from drug-using mothers to their offspring. Such paediatric infection, as noted in Chapter 6, does not necessarily lead to antibody retention. Evidence suggests that the use of illicit drugs occurs at all socioeconomic levels. Even so, heavy involvement with illicit drug use, especially the injection of opiates and other drugs, is associated with unemployment, poverty and social disadvantage (Peck and Plant 1986; Plant and Plant 1992).

CONCLUSIONS

The misuse of alcohol, tobacco and illicit drugs poses major health problems in Scotland. Levels of alcohol and illicit drug use are not remarkable, but a disproportionate number of Scots continue to smoke tobacco. The adverse consequences of illicit drug use have been greatly magnified by the advent of HIV infection. HIV/AIDS poses a massive threat to public health. In spite of this, it is emphasised that at present the greatest drug-related harm in Scotland still relates to tobacco and the misuse of alcohol.

REFERENCES

ANSWER (1991) AIDS News Supplementary Weekly Report, Glasgow,
    Communicable Diseases (Scotland) Unit, Ruchill Hospital (CDS90 and 91).
Bagnall, G. (1991) *Educating Young Drinkers*, London, Tavistock / Routledge.
Berridge, V. (ed.) (1990) *Drugs Research and Policy in Britain*, Aldershot, Avebury.
Berridge, V. and Edwards, G. (1981) *Opium and the People*, London, Allen Lane.
Brewers' Society (1991) *Statistical Handbook*, London, Brewers' Society.
Chambers, G. and Tombs, J. (eds) (1984) *The British Crime Survey, Scotland, A
    Scottish Research Study*, Edinburgh, HMSO.
Coggans, N., Shewan, D., Henderson, M., Davies, J.B. and O'Hagan, F. (1989).
    National Evaluation of Drug Education in Scotland, Centre for Occupational
    and Health Psychology, University of Strathclyde.
Crawford, A. and Plant, M.A. (1986) 'Regional variations in alcohol dependence
    rates: A conundrum', *Quarterly Journal of Social Affairs*, 2, 139–149.
Crawford, A., Plant, M.A., Kreitman, N. and Latcham, R. (1984) 'Regional
    variations in British alcohol morbidity rates: a myth uncovered?
    II: Population surveys', *British Medical Journal*, 289, 1343–1345.
Dight, E. (1976) *Scottish Drinking Habits*, London, HMSO.
Edwards, G. and Busch, C. (eds) (1981) *Drug Problems in Britain*, London,
    Academic Press.
Foster, K., Wilmot, A. and Dobbs, J. (1990) *General Household Survey 1988*,
    London, HMSO.
Home Office (1990) *Statistics of the Misuse of Drugs: Seizures and Offenders
    Dealt With, United Kingdom 1988 Area Tables*, London, Home Office.
Home Office (1991) *Statistics of the Misuse of Drugs: Addicts Notified to the
    Home Office, United Kingdom, 1990, Area Tables*, London, Home Office.
Latcham, R., Kreitman, N., Plant, M.A. and Crawford, A. (1984) 'Regional
    variations in British alcohol morbidity rates: a myth uncovered? I: Clinical
    surveys', *British Medical Journal* 289, 1341–3.
Leck, P., McEwan, J., Moreton, W. et al. (1985) *Action on Smoking at Work*,
    London, Academic Department of Community Medicine, King's College School
    of Medicine and Dentistry.
MacGregor, S. (ed.) (1989) *Drugs and British Society*, London, Tavistock /
    Routledge.
Morrison, V. (1991) 'The impact of HIV upon injecting drug users: a longitudinal
    study', *AIDS Care* 3, 193–201.
Morrison, V. and Plant, M.A. (1990) 'Drug problems and patterns of service use
    amongst illicit drug users in Edinburgh', *British Journal of Addiction* 85,
    547–54.
Mott J. (1989) 'Self-reported cannabis use in Great Britain in 1981', *British
    Journal of Addiction* 80, 30–43.
NOP Market Research Ltd (1982) 'Survey of drug use in the 15–21 age group
    undertaken by the Daily Mail', London, NOP.
Peck, D.F. and Plant, M.A. (1986) 'Unemployment and illegal drug use;
    concordant evidence from a prospective study and from national trends',
    British Medical Journal 293, 929–932.
Plant, M.A. (1987) *Drugs in Perspective*, London, Hodder and Stoughton.
Plant, M.A. and Foster, J. (1991) 'Teenagers and alcohol: results of a Scottish
    national survey', *Drug and Alcohol Dependence*, 28, 203–10.
Plant, M.A., Peck, D.F. and Samuel, E. (1985) *Alcohol, Drugs and School Leavers*,
    London, Tavistock.
Plant, M.A. and Plant, M.L. (1992) *Risk-Takers: Alcohol, Drugs, Sex and Young
    People*, London, Tavistock / Routledge.
Register General Scotland (1989) *Annual Report 1988*, Edinburgh, HMSO.
Robertson, J.R. (1987) *Heroin, AIDS and Society*, London, Hodder and Stoughton.
Royal College of Physicians (1977). *Smoking or Health*, London, Pitman Medicine.
Royal College of Physicians (1986) *Health or Smoking?* London, Pitman Medicine.

Royal College of Psychiatrists (1986) *Alcohol: Our Favourite Drug*, London, Tavistock.

Royal College of Psychiatrists (1987) *Drug Scenes*, London, Gaskell.

Sales, J., Duffy, J., Plant, M.A. and Peck, D.F. (1989) 'Alcohol consumption, cigarette sales and mortality in the United Kingdom: an analysis of the period 1970–1985', *Drug and Alcohol Dependence* 24, 155–60.

Scottish Health Education Coordinating Committee (1985) *Health Education in the Prevention of Alcohol-Related Problems*, Edinburgh.

Scottish Health Education Group (1986) *Drugs and Young People in Scotland*, Edinburgh, Scottish Health Education Group.

Scottish Office Home and Health Department (1991) Personal communication.

Strang, J. and Stimson, G.V. (eds) (1990) *AIDS and Drug Misuse*, London, Tavistock / Routledge.

Thurman, C. (1991) Personal communication.

Wilson, P. (1980) 'Drinking habits in the United Kingdom', *Population Trends*, Winter 1980, London, HMSO, 14–18.

2. The legend of drunken Scotland

DANIEL PATON

In 1877, the Dundee police force purchased a quantity of new improved barrows with double action springing to carry drunks to the police station. This is how the *Daily Telegraph* pictured the scene in Dundee:

> The drunk and incapable on a New Year's Day are not stray eccentricities who take a drop too much and steal home as silently as they may, but are really almost as numerous as the wounded in a general engagement; they succumb in ranks and platoons and need a special ambulance service to carry them to the rear.
>
> (*Daily Telegraph*, December 1877)

The modern wonders of electric telegraph and steam press quickly spread the story round the world confirming what everybody already knew – that the Scots were either the most drink-sodden people in Europe or exceeded in alcoholic excess only by the Swedes and the Lapps.

This reputation, already well established by 1877, has proved difficult to shake off, and the stereotype of drunken Scotland persists into the present day. It has influenced policy makers and academics and ensures that Scotland regularly features in comparative studies of countries with severe alcohol-related problems (Clayson 1969, Sclare 1975, Simpura 1981, Ritson 1985). When and how did Scotland acquire this reputation? Was it merited and what remains of it today?

The legend of drunken Scotland has its origins in the third, fourth and fifth decades of the nineteenth century and it was the Scots themselves who created it. This was a period of rapid industrialisation and urbanisation which disrupted the pre-industrial and social order in the areas touched by it. Grant and Ritson (1983), reviewing modern evidence, suggest that, in periods of rapid social change, people acquire new drinking habits but do not so readily abandon the old. Their hypothesis fits well the experience of the working classes of newly industrialised Scotland. Alcohol had an important place in pre-industrial society.

Drinking was universal, and outright intoxication was condoned on some occasions, but alcohol use was controlled by conventions operating through the community or by the churches. Among the population of the new industrial towns alcohol retained its old celebratory role and outright intoxication remained socially acceptable. On these established attitudes were superimposed new patterns of alcohol consumption reflecting the rhythms of industrial society. Life in the industrial towns, so well described by Smout (1986), was unbelievably harsh but industrial workers had more disposable income and were paid more frequently than their rural counterparts. Pay day and weekend binges, unconstrained by the social controls of traditional society and concentrated in the confined streets of towns with high population densities, resulted in brutal drunkenness on an unprecedented scale. Sir Archibald Alison, Sheriff of the City, described such a weekend in Glasgow in the 1830s: 'There are 10,000 men in Glasgow who get drunk on Saturday night: who are drunk all day Sunday and are in a state of half intoxication on Monday and go to work on Tuesday' (Smout 1969, pp. 389–90).

Among the middle and upper classes attitudes and practices in relation to drinking were changing even more radically and in a different direction. In the eighteenth century, heavy drinking and drunkenness had been a mark of social position (Graham 1899). By the 1850s the old days when the cream of Scottish society had drunk themselves insensible were an embarrassing memory. Alcohol was still universally used by the middle and upper classes and there were strong social pressures to drink, but drunkenness had been banished from polite society as incompatible with new ideals of propriety and respectability. New drinking patterns had emerged, characterised by moderation and restraint, discretion and control.

Such a marked divergence in patterns of alcohol use and drunken comportment could not go unnoticed. Drunkenness on the scale now experienced was a threat to public order and decency. Worse, it represented a dumb challenge to middle-class standards and values. The working man, drunk in the street, was rejecting in an open and dramatic way the virtues of thrift and foresight, prudence and responsibility which the middle classes were seeking to disseminate downwards in society. Worst of all, drunkenness raised the spectre of the failure of religion and the decline of national morality. The Scots believed themselves to be a nation of high moral standards and pure religion and vastly superior in intelligence and education to most other European nations. How could this self-belief be reconciled with the scenes on the streets of Glasgow at weekends? Public drunkenness, therefore, in the eyes of the middle classes, constituted a threat to national self-esteem and came to be seen as a symptom, if not a primary cause, of the decline of traditional morality.

The contention here is that Scotland's reputation for alcoholic excess had its origins in middle-class perceptions of working-class drinking patterns and concerns about their social and moral implications. The political and legislative reaction needs to be understood in terms of changes in attitudes to alcohol use as much as awareness of an objective increase in alcohol problems. That is not to say contemporaries were deluding themselves in seeing in Scotland the emergence of a distinctive drinking culture, although some newspapers suggested that the Dundee police barrows could see useful service in English towns. The most obvious distinguishing feature of Scottish drinking was the preference for spirits. This can be established with reasonable accuracy, indeed, historical statistics of separate Scottish alcohol consumption were better than they are today. In 1852, the Scots drank 2.36 gallons of proof spirits per capita and 7.2 gallons of beer while the English consumed 0.57 gallons of spirits and 30.6 gallons of beer (Inland Revenue 1870). In terms of alcohol ingested, the Scots actually drank less, 7.83 litres of absolute alcohol per capita per annum compared to 8.84 litres in England. The Scots continued to prefer whisky into the twentieth century. Im 1990 they consumed approximately sixty-one per cent of their alcohol in whisky and thirty-nine per cent in beer compared to the English twenty-seven per cent in spirits and seventy-three per cent in beer, although by this time the difference in the alcohol intake of the two countries had actually widened (Wilson 1940). Where was the evidence for drunken Scotland here? It was assumed that concentration was more important than quantity and that whisky was bound to be more potent in producing more rapid intoxication and more harmful consequences, than beer. 'It is obvious', concluded the Royal Commission on the licensing laws in 1899 'that the national drink of Scotland is more potent in producing disorderly drunkenness, than the national beverage of England' (1899, p. 175) It is now accepted that the effects of alcohol are not just a function of the quantity and concentration of the drink consumed but depend upon the culturally defined expectations of the drinker (McAndrew and Egerton 1970). John Dunlop, founder of the temperance movement, believed that the conventions and rituals surrounding drinking in Scotland caused the individual to surrender control of his drinking to the group (Dunlop 1829). Others came to the conclusion that intoxication was a deliberate aim for many working men: 'Among the working classes of the Lowlands, tipsiness is a state of pleasure to be looked forward to with avidity, to be gained as rapidly as possible and maintained for as long as possible' (Geikie 1904, p. 312).

Attitudes to alcohol continued to change over the second half of the nineteenth century. An unremitting barrage of temperance propaganda sought to make alcohol use unacceptable in society. It did not succeed, while it did help to shape attitudes and behaviour. The contention that drink was an enormous evil intimately linked to almost every major social problem, gained wide acceptance in Scotland. That section of society most intimately involved in drink-related social problems was least influenced by such theories, but those who had pretensions to moral leadership were. In 1850, the entire body of teetotal Church ministers in Scotland would not have filled a pew. By 1900, fifty per cent of Scottish ministers claimed to abstain entirely from alcohol (Scottish Temperance League 1900). The Scottish Temperance League survey which provided this information was comprehensive, though doubtless there were problems with the truthfulness of respondents as there are with any survey. All the same, the result is a significant pointer to attitudes to alcohol and patterns of consumption among the Scottish middle classes. The ministry was still a group with prestige and social influence, and provided a useful barometer of middle class values. It would be too much to claim that the Scottish middle classes became teetotallers in large numbers like their American counterparts. Total abstinence was most commonly found amongst the lower middle class and the more prosperous manual workers, the C2s in modern parlance. Rather, the pattern of moderate drinking established earlier in the century was reinforced and became even more discreet and controlled. By the beginning of the twentieth century drinkers in Scotland were on the defensive rather as smokers are today. Drinking, among those who valued their respectability, was becoming an activity carried out by consenting adults in private.

In the first decade of the twentieth century the anti-drink forces in Scotland reached the peak of their power and influence. They had won the argument over drink and captured the minds, if not always the hearts and stomachs, of respectable Scots. Temperance reform had penetrated the churches, the guardians of the nation's morals and the Liberal party which dominated Scottish politics. Many of the leaders of the emerging labour and socialist movement were teetotallers. A formidable anti-drink coalition had been assembled. This explains why the Scottish licensing system became the most restrictive in Britain and why Scotland, alone among the countries of the UK, experienced a form of prohibition under the Temperance (Scotland) Act of 1913. By the time the Act came into force in 1920, the great days of the temperance movement were over. Even so, in the local option campaign of 1920, nearly forty per cent of the electorate voted to close their local public houses immediately and without compensation. By the beginning of the twentieth century, many Scots, having convinced themselves that their country was peculiarly cursed by the evils of drink, had reacted strongly against it. Society was polarised on the question of alcohol use, and in this respect Scotland resembles the Scandinavian countries rather than England.

In the history of Scottish drinking, the interwar period appears as an interlude between the end of the anti-drink advance which began in the nineteenth century and the dismantling of the Victorian system of restriction which began in the 1960s. The interwar period should be seen as a watershed. Underneath the apparent stalemate, important changes were taking place in attitudes to alcohol and in drinking habits which were not apparent until much later. Scotland immediately after the First World War was still a hostile place for drink-sellers. The 1920 Licensing Act consolidated wartime restrictions on opening hours. Local authorities were embarking on a policy of reducing the number of licences, and Glasgow under the 1890 Resolution excluded them from council-owned property (Checkland 1976). Local Option was about to come into force, which threatened publicans with the loss of their licences without compensation. All these policies were designed to reduce alcohol consumption by limiting access to its retail sale. Public houses, closed on Sundays since 1853, were now open on average for seven hours on weekdays. Alcohol consumption, which had been falling before the war, fell steeply as a result of high taxation and postwar unemployment in industrial areas. By the 1930s, average consumption in Scotland had levelled out at about four litres of alcohol per capita per annum (Wilson 1940). A bottle of whisky cost approximately a day's wage for a manual worker in industry, if he was lucky enough to have a job. Falling alcohol consumption was accompanied by a decline in all indices of measurable alcohol-related problems, including drunkenness and violent offences (Wilson 1940). Alcohol could no longer be credibly portrayed as a threat to public order, and temperance spokesmen sought to redefine the drink problem as a problem of public health. Falling alcohol consumption may have damaged the drink trade but it had removed the raison d'être of the anti-drink forces. Popular support for temperance declined rapidly as social reformers developed new priorities. By the 1930s drink had ceased to be a major issue on the agenda of political debate and social concern. When drink consumption began to rise again in the 1950s there was no culture of abstinence and no organised political opposition to campaign against it.

Decades of low alcohol consumption and the removal of drink from the social agenda helped to account for the discontinuity between the drinking cultures of nineteenth-century Scotland and those of Scotland today. In 1930, the report of the Royal Commission on the licensing laws concluded that 'a younger generation is growing up to which, as a whole any resort to alcoholic excess as a necessary or usual practice is almost entirely unknown' (p. 12–13).

The attitudes, myths and rituals of the drinking culture of industrial Scotland were not being passed on to the next generation. The decline of the old hard-drinking tradition was fittingly marked by Hugh Mac-

Diarmid's splendid essay 'The Dour Drinkers of Glasgow' in which he lamented the shift from whisky to beer and deplored the changes threatening the cheerless functionality of the traditional Scottish pub (MacDiarmid 1952). As alcohol consumption rose in the 1960s, a different, more homogeneous drinking culture emerged, shaped by contemporary attitudes and commercial pressures. Working-class drinking no longer threatened public order or outraged moral standards to which few now adhered. The middle classes, liberated from earlier notions of respectability and propriety, began to rediscover the pub. Women, defying more deeply rooted taboos, also began to drink in public. Across the divides of class and sex, drinking patterns were becoming more similar, although there were still very significant differences. Beer, or rather lager, became the working man's drink. Women did most to keep up the old Scottish preference for hard liquor (Simpura 1981).

By the 1970s the vast majority of Scots were drinkers and alcohol had regained an almost universal acceptance not known in Scotland for a century (Dight 1976). Divergent drinking patterns and polarised attitudes to alcohol use were no longer such a marked characteristic of Scottish society. In those circumstances it is not surprising that the licensing laws, products of the fears and prejudices of another age, should have seemed ripe for reform. A more liberal licensing system was sometimes justified as a necessary measure to civilise the drinking habits of the Scots. Perhaps it was a recognition that the Scots were becoming in their drinking habits, not very different from the English (Wilson 1980).

Did the nineteenth-century Scots deserve their reputation as a nation peculiarly afflicted by alcohol? Probably they did, for while they may have consumed less alcohol than the English, the industrial working class had devised a style of drinking unmatched in the United Kingdom for self-destructive intensity. Society's reaction, however, has to be explained in terms of perceptions and attitudes as much as the actual magnitude of the problem. What else can explain why the rapid increase in alcohol consumption and alcohol-related problems in modern Scotland aroused little social concern? Drink was by then no longer perceived to be a threat to society's moral foundations or subversive of its dominant social values. That role had been taken over by other drugs.

What remains of Scotland's alcoholic notoriety? The drinking habits of modern Scots may be little different from the English, yet the incidence of alcohol-related problems is relatively high (Crawford and Plant 1986). Is this because 'half the Scots are (still) drinking the other half's share' (Laurance 1984)? Or is it because practices of identifying and recording alcohol- related problems themselves reflect distinctive national traditions? Has the removal of restrictions on access to alcohol, the legacy of the nineteenth century anti-alcohol campaign, affected these problems for better or worse? The drink question may not be the great issue it once was, but alcohol retains its ability to cause controversy and inspire research in Scotland, and this interest in drinking and its consequences is an enduring legacy of Scotland's alcoholic past.

REFERENCES

Checkland, S.G. (1976) *The Upas Tree 0 – Glasgow 1875–1976*, Glasgow.
Clayson, C. (1976) 'The medico – social aspects of liquor licensing', *Scottish Medical Journal* 21, 175–81.
Crawford, A. and Plant, M.A. (1986) 'Regional variations in alcohol dependence rates: A conundrum', *Quarterly Journal of Social Affairs* 2, 139–49.
Dight, E. (1976) *Scottish Drinking Habits*, London, HMSO.
Dunlop, J. (1829) *The Artificial and Compulsory Drinking Usages of North Britain*, Greenock.
Geikie, Sir A. (1904) *Scottish Reminiscences*, Glasgow, J. Maclehose and Son.
Graham, H.G. (1899) *The Social Life of Scotland in the eighteenth century*, London.
Grant M., and Ritson, E.B. (1983) *The Prevention Debate*, London, Croon Helm.
Inland Revenue Report (1870) P.P. 1870 XX.
Laurance, J. (1984) 'Drinking, Scottish style', *New Society*, 16 August 125–27.
McAndrew, C. and Egerton, R.B. (1970) *Drunken Comportment; A Social Explanation*, London, Nebon.
MacDiarmid, H. (1952) 'The Dour Drinkers of Glasgow', *The American Mercury*.
Ritson, E.B. (1984) *Community Response to Alcohol-Related Problems*, Geneva, World Health Organization.
Royal Commission on the Liquor Licensing Laws (1899) P.P. 1899 XXXV.
Royal Commission on Licensing (Scotland) (1931) P.P. 1930/31 XV.
Sclare, A.B. (1975) 'Drinking habits in Scotland', *International Journal of Offender Therapy and Comparative Criminology* 19, 241–9.
Scottish Temperance League Register (1900) Glasgow.
Simpura J. (1981) 'Drinking habits in Finland and Scotland', *International Journal of Addictions* 16, 1129–41.
Smout, T.C. (1969) *A History of the Scottish People, 1560–1830*, London, Collins.
Smout, T.C. (1986) *A Century of the Scottish People 1830–1950*, London, Collins.

3. Alcohol and health

PETER W. BRUNT

Sir Andrew Clark, physician to Queen Victoria, once described alcohol as 'a poison – so is strychnine; so is arsenic; so is opium. It ranks with these agents. Health is always in some way or other injured by it.' The idea that alcoholic beverages are dangerous is not new. The social harm from alcohol was well described in ancient civilisations (the Bible contains numerous references) as were its dependence-producing qualities. An ancient Chinese proverb goes:

First the man takes the drink ...
then the drink takes the man.

Yet Clark was ahead of his time in some ways – in placing alcohol in its proper place along with other drugs of dependence and in pointing out the potential toxicity of alcohol. Indeed, the direct linking of alcohol to 'toxic damage' was a late revelation and even the insight of Matthew Baillie (Baillie 1812) could only *associate* the 'long process of drinking spiritous liquors' with the development of cirrhosis without implying cause as such. Recently, evidence has accumulated to suggest that *moderate* regular alcohol consumption may have a potentially advantageous effect; so perhaps all is not complete gloom.

In some ways, the Scots have shown unique features in their use of alcohol and in the adverse consequences it produces. Furthermore, Scots scientists and Scots clinicians have figured significantly in the literature pertaining to alcohol usage and its effects and Scotland can be proud of its contribution in the field. Some of this contribution is referred to in this brief review.

The Celts made wide usage of meads and ales, the latter largely produced from barley. Hops were a relatively late introduction into Britain (around 1520 AD), and many distinctive Scottish additives in brewing are recorded; in the Highlands heathers and broom, in the Western Isles white carrot seeds, for example. Some additives could

3. Alcohol and health

PETER W. BRUNT

Sir Andrew Clark, physician to Queen Victoria, once described alcohol as 'a poison – so is strychnine; so is arsenic; so is opium. It ranks with these agents. Health is always in some way or other injured by it.' The idea that alcoholic beverages are dangerous is not new. The social harm from alcohol was well described in ancient civilisations (the Bible contains numerous references) as were its dependence-producing qualities. An ancient Chinese proverb goes:

First the man takes the drink ...
then the drink takes the man.

Yet Clark was ahead of his time in some ways – in placing alcohol in its proper place along with other drugs of dependence and in pointing out the potential toxicity of alcohol. Indeed, the direct linking of alcohol to 'toxic damage' was a late revelation and even the insight of Matthew Baillie (Baillie 1812) could only *associate* the 'long process of drinking spiritous liquors' with the development of cirrhosis without implying cause as such. Recently, evidence has accumulated to suggest that *moderate* regular alcohol consumption may have a potentially advantageous effect; so perhaps all is not complete gloom.

In some ways, the Scots have shown unique features in their use of alcohol and in the adverse consequences it produces. Furthermore, Scots scientists and Scots clinicians have figured significantly in the literature pertaining to alcohol usage and its effects and Scotland can be proud of its contribution in the field. Some of this contribution is referred to in this brief review.

The Celts made wide usage of meads and ales, the latter largely produced from barley. Hops were a relatively late introduction into Britain (around 1520 AD), and many distinctive Scottish additives in brewing are recorded; in the Highlands heathers and broom, in the Western Isles white carrot seeds, for example. Some additives could easily have been toxic. Some distilled liquor was in use as early as the twelfth century, apparently for medicinal purposes, but Scotland's unique liquor, whisky, was a relatively late sixteenth century development. Led by example and encouragement from the monarchs downward, alcohol consumption throughout Britain rose to record heights in the Seventeenth and Eighteenth Centuries, especially with the manufacture and import of cheap spirits. In 1708, the first year when records of manufacture were kept in Scotland, some 50,844 gallons of spirit were produced. Just over one hundred years later, the Scots people were consuming 5,777,000 gallons annually. Licensing of distillation, introduced into Scotland in 1782, did little to curb the increase, and it was rising public anger that led to the great temperance backlash which reached its peak in the mid- to late-nineteenth century. This is elaborated in Chapter 2.

The problems related to the misuse of alcohol, especially social and public order problems, seem to have been recognised early. Taxation and controls on brewing were well established by the twelfth century, and acts of Parliament in Scotland in 1436 and 1492 limited the opening of alehouses and controlled the adulteration of ales and wines – a recognition, possibly, of the potential dangers to health. Yet attitudes toward alcohol and its health-damaging effects remained remarkably ambivalent (as they still are). Alarmed at the prospect of the reopening of their local malt distillery towards the end of the eighteenth century the good folk of Leadhills in Lanarkshire wrote: 'the malt distilleries have been the principal cause of the immoderate use of spirituous liquors which has been found by experience highly detrimental not only to the health but also to the morals of mankind' (Cherrington 1929, p. 2386). By contrast, a Scottish doctor writing in the first years of the nineteenth century said: 'In my father's day and long after doctors and every other person were satisfied that health depended greatly on the quantity of "good" liquor a person swallowed daily' (Cherrington 1929, p. 2386). This curious ambivalence persists to the present day in all strands of society, including the health professions, and Scotland is no exception, some aspects of its 'drinking culture' being in this respect distinctive, even unique.

The temperance movements had only a limited effect, and it was the legislation, supply limitations and other pressures surrounding the two World Wars that had a dramatic impact on consumption. As noted in Chapter 1, per capita consumption in the United Kingdom has risen considerably since World War Two. In association with the rise, there has been an increase in alcohol-related health and other problems.

ALCOHOL AND TISSUE DAMAGE

It is the ethyl alcohol in alcoholic beverages which accounts for the injury to tissues and organs; congeners and additives have only a very limited role, although in certain circumstances they may have some significance. Alcohol, because of its physico-chemical properties, is very rapidly absorbed and distributed in tissues throughout the body. Some metabolic breakdown occurs in the stomach and bowel mucosal lining during absorption and some subsequently in other tissues – but predominantly in the liver, where it is 'burned' preferentially to other energy substrates. The result is tissue damage that reflects a complex interplay of toxic effects and nutritional factors. For most people with modest habits, this 'damage' is transitory and rapidly 'repaired' but in some individuals a combination of excess consumption and background susceptibility (partly genetic and sex-determined, partly nutritional, partly due to additional injuries) leads to sustained damage. The liver itself may be damaged to produce fatty change, hepatitis and ultimately cirrhosis. The pancreas gland may be inflamed (pancreatitis) and calcified. Damage to alimentary mucosal lining may lead to bleeding or, more long term, to impaired absorption of nutrients. Complex toxic and nutritional changes lead to characteristic brain damage (atrophy, Wernicke-Korsakoff syndrome and other conditions). Blood pressure commonly rises and contributes to an increased risk of stroke especially in young people, in whom alcohol is the commonest cause. Disturbances of heart rhythm and damage to both heart and skeletal muscle occur. Effects upon the blood are common, sexual function may be impaired and bone thinning may also be caused. Even the foetus in utero may be affected by heavy maternal drinking. This is elaborated in Chapter 4. Acute intoxication endangers life and health by causing coma, fits and injuries. A similar 'indirect' effect of alcohol consumption is the increased risk of HIV/AIDS infection (Plant 1990). This topic is discussed in Chapter 5. Finally, an interesting link between alcohol and certain forms of cancer (larynx, pharynx and oesophagus associated with smoking, liver associated with cirrhosis, and breast cancer) has now been established though is not yet fully understood.

In the metabolism, alcohol is first broken down to acetaldehyde, which is then further oxidised to acetate and finally to carbon dioxide and water. Acetaldehyde is a much more reactive and dangerous substance than ethyl alcohol, and evidence points strongly to its accumulation being the principal source of damage to cells and tissues.

CONSUMPTION OF ALCOHOL

There is ample evidence now that the pattern and degree of observed physical problems and ill-health in a community reflect to a considerable extent the levels and patterns of alcohol consumption. Some inherent racial differences seem to occur, but, except in rather obvious situations such as the susceptibility to flushing in the Japanese, these differences are of minimal significance. As will be seen, however, inexplicable discordance between consumption and certain alcohol problems, even between regions within Britain, occurs not uncommonly (Kilich and Plant 1981). Recent evidence suggests that distinct, but fairly modest regional variations in alcohol use and misuse do exist (Crawford and Plant 1980).

The Scots have an unenviable reputation for drinking more than the rest of the UK. In fact, the data do not support this widely held belief (Wilson 1980), although it does seem that expenditure on alcohol is higher in Scottish households than south of the Border (Scottish Council on Alcohol 1988). Wide UK regional variations in consumption are well recognised (Cummins et al. 1981), and a survey in four towns – Inverness, Aberdeen, Ayr and Glasgow – confirmed this phenomenon in Scotland (Plant and Pirie 1979). Population surveys depend, of course, heavily upon self-reporting, and there is often wide variance with figures calculated from excise returns. Nevertheless, such surveys give interesting and important insights into variations of drinking habits which may have relevance in explaining the problems deriving from drinking, including health problems. Scotland has some important distinctive features in its drinking patterns by age, sex, occupation, social class, religion and beverage type (Dight 1976; Plant 1979; Chick 1982; Plant Peck, and Stuart 1982). For example, Scottish men drink more of their alcohol as spirits than their English and Welsh counterparts and tend to drink less often but more at a time, especially at weekends (Wilson 1980). This is perhaps surprising when one considers the patterns of cirrhosis mortality (vide infra) and the widely accepted belief that alcoholic cirrhosis is more likely to result from continuous heavy drinking rather than binge drinking (Brunt 1988). One fact stands out. Alcohol consumption in the UK, involving all types of beverage, has risen sharply in the last thirty years (being 4.491 litres pure alcohol/annum/head total in 1963 and 7.465 litres pure alcohol/annum/head total in 1987). This has both immediate and longer-term significance for the nation's health.

ALCOHOL IMPACT UPON HEALTH

Assessing the impact of alcohol upon health can be done in several ways. Surveying the frequency of problem drinking among hospital inpatients has provided some alarming results in Scotland. In one Glasgow hospital (the Victoria Infirmary), a study of 323 consecutive male medical emergency admissions showed that almost one in five had an important alcohol component and about one quarter had evidence of problem drinking (Quinn and Johnston 1976). Similar figures have emerged since from other centres in both Scotland and south of the Border. Chick and his colleagues found that 161 (twenty-two per cent) out of a total of 731 male medical admissions to Edinburgh Royal Infirmary met their criteria for problem drinking (Chick et al. 1985). This does not, of course,

Adverse drug reactions	24%
Chest pain (including coronary heart disease)	18%
Convulsions	7%
Respiratory disorders	7%
Alimentary disorders	17%

(Source: Brunt 1991)

Table 3.1 Primary (admitting) diagnosis in patients where 'alcohol dependence / alcohol problems' also identified as secondary diagnosis (Aberdeen Hospitals – Medical Wards)

imply that twenty-two per cent of admissions are *due* to alcohol-related disease, but does point to the *contribution* that alcohol makes to physical ill health. However, the same group later showed in their survey from Edinburgh Royal Infirmary and a local male control community survey (Lloyd et al. 1986) that rising alcohol consumption was associated with an increased risk of admission for certain categories of illness, including liver disorders, upper gastrointestinal disease, myocardial infarction, other myocardial diseases and respiratory disorders. They used a measure of risk controlling for age, i.e. the logarithm of the odds ratio (Chick et al. 1986). Gastritis, bleeding and pancreatitis, disorders strongly linked to binge drinking, featured not surprisingly in the higher categories of alcohol intake. This study lends strong support to the view that increasing consumption is associated with increasing risk of physical damage without the need to postulate some special group 'at risk'. The results are also in line with similar data relating risk and consumption for various 'alcohol-related' physical disorders from around the world, including the classic studies from France and Germany (Pequignot et al. 1978; Lelbach 1975).

In some patients admitted to hospital with evidence of problem drinking, the primary 'admitting' diagnosis may not, of course, give any lead to the alcohol abuse, hence the value of screening questionnaires and/or blood tests, especially where a high index of suspicion arouses pursuit. In one survey of medical hospital admissions in which alcohol misuse was identified as a secondary diagnosis 'drug problems' was the most frequently found diagnosis, with chest pain and 'alimentary disorders' trailing second. This is elaborated in Table 3.1.

A similar approach to assessing the volume of impact of alcohol abuse on the hospital services can be used in other 'high-risk' departments. Accidents and injuries are a major group in this category, and an important study also from Edinburgh found that as many as forty per cent of cases at the Accident and Emergency Department had been drinking. As would be expected, figures were higher for those with a primary label of 'assault', 'trauma', 'suicide attempt' etc. than for those with medical or surgical conditions, although even for those categories the proportion was approximately twenty per cent (Holt et al. 1980).

Alternatively, one can look at a specific disease accepted to be alcohol-related and measure the contribution alcohol makes to its epidemiology. The best and classic example is liver cirrhosis. Since Jellinek proposed its use as a 'marker' (Jolliffe and Jellinek 1942), mortality rates for all forms of cirrhosis together have been employed to estimate consumption rates within the population. However, wide variations occur which are not always easy to explain. In Scotland, crude rates per 100,000 vary from 1.8 to 8.1, the highest reported rates being in the Glasgow area closely followed by Highland Region (Kilich and Plant 1981). However, reported mortality (and morbidity) rates are subject to all sorts of errors, mainly leading to under-reporting. Moreover, alcohol accounts for only a proportion of all cirrhosis, probably between a half and two thirds in Britain (Sherlock et al. 1971; Saunders et al. 1981). In a study of cirrhosis mortality rates in Scotland between 1979 and 1984 Kreitman and Duffy have shown that alcoholic and non-alcoholic cirrhosis have quite distinct epidemiological profiles and must be considered separately to be of value (Kreitman and Duffy 1989). It is known that in Scotland deaths from alcoholic cirrhosis in both males and females have been rising sharply in recent years (and are probably continuing to do so) while non-alcoholic disease has fluctuated only mildly (Duffy and Latcham 1986).

There seems no reason to doubt the association between rising consumption of alcohol and cirrhosis deaths but the collateral factors which are at play are not so easily understood. Certainly, the rise in cirrhosis mortality has been steady over at least twenty years and was not noticeably affected in either direction by the changes in Scottish licensing laws in 1976 (Duffy and Plant 1986). This topic is reviewed in Chapter 11. Changes in consumption do however reflect changes in price related to disposable income, and a study in the Lothian Region of Scotland suggests that this affects all grades of drinker (Kendell et al. 1983).

It is also of great interest that not only cirrhosis mortality rates but also the *patterns* of liver disease vary in different regions of Scotland. For example, alcoholic hepatitis is observed more frequently in Glasgow than in other centres (Hislop et al. 1983). Unfortunately morbidity data for all forms of alcohol related disease are even less reliable than mortality statistics since they depend heavily upon hospital-acquired data with the inevitable bias introduced.

Also unfortunately, although it may be possible that Scotland's apparently higher propensity to alcohol-related liver damage is genetically determined, it has not so far been possible to show this by the use of known markers (Mills et al. 1988).

ALCOHOL AND HEALTH?

Is there a positive side to the story; is it all a question of ill health? Heavy alcohol consumption (often accompanied, as it is, by heavy smoking) is positively associated with death from ischaemic (coronary) heart disease (CHD), but it has been suggested that light drinking may conversely have a mildly protective effect. This seems intuitively a feasible proposition, since alcohol has been shown to cause a rise in the type of cholesterol with a protective quality circulating in the blood stream – so-called High-Density Lipoprotein Cholesterol. In their study of hospital admissions in Edinburgh, Chick et al. (1986) found that occasional (less than weekly) consumers had a higher mortality from CHD than all but the heaviest drinkers (the U-shaped curve), but they were probably the first to recognise the intrinsic fallacy in the curve. Subsequent analyses have emphasised the point – that abstainers and very low-drinking groups are likely to be weighted with the ill and those who have reduced their drinking for health reasons (Shaper 1990). In fact, recent studies have eliminated some of the flaws in the study designs and still suggest a potential benefit of a daily intake of one or two units (Jackson et al. 1991; Rimm et al. 1991). But do the potential benefits outweigh the potential disadvantages? Marmot has concluded that while the evidence suggests that two drinks a day are associated with no cardiovascular harm and may be protective against CHD, 'the balance of harm and benefit does not weigh in favour of making a recommendation to the public to drink in order to prevent coronary heart disease' (Marmot and Brunner 1991).

THE PUBLIC HEALTH IMPLICATIONS OF ALCOHOL USE AND ABUSE

Marmot's caveat on the suggested benefits of modest drinking is wise and illustrates the difficulties facing educators and health promoters in a society with colossal ambivalence towards alcohol problems, in a culture where alcohol figures richly in images of maturity, sexuality and sociability. Most of the educators, researchers and health promoters like their drink. The medical Royal Colleges have agreed upon guidelines of (relatively) 'low-' and 'high-risk' levels of drinking. Many, however, exceed these recommendations; for example, a recent survey on lifestyle in the Grampian region of Scotland showed that twenty per cent of men and ten per cent of women respondents admitted consumption above the 'low-risk' category of twenty-one units weekly for men and fourteen for women (Grampian Health Board 1991). (A unit contains 7.95 grams/1 centilitre of absolute alcohol. This is roughly equivalent to a single public house measure of spirits, or a single glass of wine or to half a pint of normal-strength beer, lager, cider or stout.) Reducing alcohol intake within the community overall is a declared aim of the World Health

Organization in *Health for All 2000*, the means including fiscal measures, licensing restrictions and education (World Health Organization
1980). But the Ledermann concept that there is a relation between *mean*
consumption and the prevalence of heavy drinking has been challenged,
among others, by Duffy (1989). However, Kreitman (1986) has drawn
attention to an important concept in health promotion – that the relatively small group of really heavy drinkers (men consuming over fifty
units per week and women consuming over thirty-five units per week)
are not simply the groups most likely to be hard to influence but they
also contribute fewer overall 'problems' to the community pool of alcohol
damage than do the moderate drinkers. Drawing his conclusions from
three important studies, all of them from Scotland (although in only one
of them were health problems as such included in the indicators of
alcohol harm), Kreitman applied the concept of the 'Preventive Paradox'
in which the target area shifts away from the most obvious group
(Kreitman 1986; Crawford et al. 1984; Crawford et al. 1985; Ritson
1985). This changes the emphasis in alcohol health promotion from a
categorical model to a dimensional model and challenges *all* drinkers in
society. Although the validity of this concept in strictly disease-related
contexts needs to be tested (and the long time-frame necessary makes
this difficult), it seems entirely reasonable to extrapolate it to physical
health and advise a general reduction in alcohol intake by society.

CONCLUSIONS

What then should one conclude about alcohol and health in Scotland?
The picture is not an unsullied one. If the inexorable rise of cirrhosis
mortality and its consistent elevation above the UK level are indicators
of alcohol harm in general the outlook is not happy. Yet, in the last two
decades, Scotland has shown an excellent record in provision of professional and voluntary counselling, in health promotion and in research.
Without any surrender to complacency perhaps one may soon be able to
say, with Iago in *Othello*:

> Come, come – good wine is a good familiar creature, *if it be well
> us'd*; exclaim no more against it.

REFERENCES

Baillie, M. (1812) *The Morbid Anatomy of Some Parts of the Human Body*, London, Bulmer, 101.

Brunt, P. (1988) 'The Liver and Alcohol', *Journal of Hepatology* 7, 377–383.

Brunt, P. (1991) 'Admissions to Medical Wards with Alcohol Problems' (Unpublished data).

Cherrington, E.H. (ed.) (1929) *Standard Encylopedia of the Alcohol Problem*, Westerville, Ohio, Newton-Simons.

Chick, J. (1982) 'Epidemiology of alcohol use and its hazards', *British Medical Bulletin* 38, 3–8.

Chick, J., Lloyd, G. and Crombie, E. (1985) 'Counselling problem drinkers in medical wards: a controlled study', *British Medical Journal* 290, 965–7.

Chick, J., Lloyd, G.G., Duffy, J.C. and Ritson, B. (1986) 'Medical admissions in men: the risk among drinkers', *Lancet* 2, 1380–3.

Crawford, A. and Plant, M.A. (1986) 'Regional variations in alcohol dependence rates: a conundrum', *Quarterly Journal of Social Affairs* 2, 139–44.

Crawford, A., Plant, M.A., Kreitman, N. and Latcham, R. (1984) Regional variations in British alcohol morbidity rates: a myth uncovered? 2 – Population surveys, *British Medical Journal* 289, 1343-9.

Crawford, A., Plant, M., Kreitman, N. and Latcham, R. (1985) Self reported alcohol consumption and adverse consequences of drinking in three areas of Britain: general population studies, *British Journal of Addiction* 80, 421–8.

Cummins, R.O., Shaper, A.G., Walker, M. and Wale, C.J. (1981) 'Smoking and drinking by middle-aged British men: effects of social class and town of residence', *British Medical Journal* 283, 1497–1502.

Dight, S.E. (1976) *Scottish Drinking Habits*, London, HMSO.

Duffy, J.C. and Latcham, R. (1986) 'Liver cirrhosis mortality in England and Wales compared to Scotland: an age-period cohort analysis 1941–81', *Journal of the Royal Statistical Society* series A 149, 45–9.

Duffy, J.C. and Plant, M.A. (1986) 'Scotland's liquor licensing changes: an assessment', *British Medical Journal* 292, 36–9.

Grampian Health Board (1991) *Towards a Healthier Grampian Lifestyle*, Aberdeen, Grampian Health Board.

Hislop, W.S., Bouchier, I.A.D., Allan, J.G., Brunt, P.W., Eastwood, M., Finlayson, N.D.C., James, O., Russell, R.I. and Watkinson, G. (1983) 'Alcoholic liver disease in Scotland and north-eastern England: Presenting Features in 510 Patients', *Quarterly Journal of Medicine* 206, 232–43.

Holt, S., Stewart, I.C., Dixon, J.M.J., Elton, R.A., Taylor, T.V. and Little, K. (1980) 'Alcohol and the emergency service patient', *British Medical Journal* 281, 638–40.

Jackson, R., Scragg, R. and Beaglehole, R. (1991) 'Alcohol consumption and risk of coronary heart disease', *British Medical Journal* 303, 211–16.

Jolliffe, N. and Jellinek, E. (1942) 'Cirrhosis of the Liver', in Jellinek, E.M. (ed) *Effects of Alcohol on the Individual*, Yale University Press, New Haven, Vol. I, 273–324.

Kendell, R.E., de Roumanie, M. and Ritson, E.B. (1983) 'Effect of economic changes on Scottish drinking habits 1978–1982', *British Journal of Addiction* 78, 365–79.

Kilich, S. and Plant, M.A. (1981) 'Regional variations in the levels of alcohol-related problems in Britain', *British Journal of Addiction* 76, 47–62.

Kreitman, N. and Duffy, J.C. (1989) 'Alcoholic and non-alcoholic liver disease in relation to alcohol consumption in Scotland 1978–1984, Part I epidemiology of liver diseases', *British Journal of Addiction* 84, 607–18.

Kreitman, N. (1986) 'Alcohol consumption and the Preventive Paradox', *British Journal of Addiction* 81, 353–63.

Lelbach, W.K. (1975) 'Cirrhosis in the alcoholic and its relation to the volume of alcohol abuse', *Annals of the New York Academy of Sciences* 252, 85–105.

Lloyd, G., Chick, J., Crombie, E. and Anderson, S. (1986) 'Problem drinkers in medical wards, consumption patterns and disabilities in newly identified male cases', *British Journal of Addiction* 81, 785–92.

Marmot, M. and Brunner, E. (1991) 'Alcohol and cardiovascular disease: the status of the U-shaped curve', *British Medical Journal* 303, 565–8.

Mills, P.R., Macsween, R.N.M., Dick, H.M. and Hislop, W.S. (1988) 'Histocompatibility antigens in patients with alcoholic liver disease in Scotland and north-eastern England: failure to show an association', *Gut* 29, 146–8.

Pequignot, G., Tuyns, A.J. and Berta, J.L. (1978) 'Ascitic cirrhosis in relation to alcohol consumption', *International Journal of Epidemiology* 7, 113–20.

Plant, M.A. (1979) 'Occupations, drinking patterns and alcohol related problems: conclusions from a follow-up study', *British Journal of Addiction* 74, 267–73.

Plant, M.A. (1990) 'Alcohol, sex and AIDS', *Alcohol and Alcoholism* 25, 293–301.

Plant, M.A. and Peck, D.F. and Stuart, R. (1982) 'Self-reported drinking habits and alcohol-related consequences among a cohort of Scottish teenagers', *British Journal of Addiction* 77, 75–90.

Plant, M.A. and Pirie, F. (1979) 'Self-reported alcohol consumption and alcohol related problems: a study in four Scottish towns', *Social Psychiatry* 14, 65–73.

Quinn, M.A. and Johnston, R.V. (1976) 'Alcohol problems in acute male admissions', *Health Bulletin* 34, 253–6.

Rimm, E.B., Gicvannucci, E.L., Willett, W.C., Colditz, G.A., Ascherio, A., Rosner, B. and Stampfer, M.J. (1991) 'Prospective study of alcohol consumption and risk of coronary disease in men', *Lancet* 338, 464–7.

Ritson, E.B. (1985) 'A community response to alcohol-related problems', World Health Organization, Geneva, Public Health Papers No. 81.

Saunders, J.B., Walters, J.R.F., Davies, P. and Paton, A. (1981) 'A 20-year prospective study of cirrhosis', *British Medical Journal* 282, 263–6.

Scottish Council on Alcohol (1988) *Alcohol Statistics*, Glasgow, Scottish Council on Alcohol, p. 21.

Shaper, A.G. (1990) 'Alcohol and mortality: a review of prospective studies', *British Journal of Addiction* 85, 837–47.

Sherlock, S., Brunt, P. and Scheuer, P. (1971) 'Clinical and pathological aspects of alcoholic liver disease', in Gerok, W., Sickinger, K. and Hennekauser, H.H. (eds) *Alkohol und Leber*, F.K. Schaffauer, Stuttgart.

Wilson, D. (1980) 'Drinking habits in the United Kingdom', *Population Trends* 22, 14–18.

World Health Organization (1980) *Problems Related to Alcoholic Consumption*, Technical Report Series No. 650, World Health Organization, Geneva.

4. Alcohol, drugs, tobacco and pregnancy

MOIRA PLANT

The possible adverse effects of alcohol or other drugs on human pregnancy have been noted in ancient folklore and in religious texts. This
topic has also received more recent scientific attention. Sullivan (1899)
reported that the children of 'inebriate mothers' were more likely to be
stillborn or to die in early infancy. The offspring of opium-using mothers
in eighteenth-century Britain were described as 'poor wizened, ill-nour-
ished' and 'pitiable to behold' (Berridge and Edwards 1981). The famous
Edinburgh physician Thomas Trotter (1813) referred to the possible ill
effects of maternal heavy drinking during pregnancy in his celebrated
essay on the effects of alcohol on the human body. Haggard and Jellinek
(1942) and Montague (1965) concluded, however, that evidence did not
support the conclusion that maternal drinking during pregnancy was
harmful to the developing foetus.

ALCOHOL

During the 1950s and 1960s several studies reported evidence of an
association between heavy drinking by pregnant women and birth
defects (e.g. Roquette 1957; Christiaens 1961). Lemoine et al. (1968)
described the results of a French study. This noted that the offspring of
alcohol-dependent parents were characterised by low intelligence and
low birth weight, short height, slow growth and linguistic problems.
Several researchers from the USA reported that the offspring of alcohol-
abusing mothers exhibited a failure to thrive (Ulleland, Wennberg, Igo
and Smith 1970; Ulleland 1972).

Jones and Smith (1973) in association with Ulleland, suggested a
term to describe the characteristics noted among the babies of alcohol-
dependent mothers. This was the *Fetal Alcohol Syndrome*. These
authors suggested that this syndrome included pre- and postnatal
growth deficiencies, developmental delays, short palpebral fissure size,

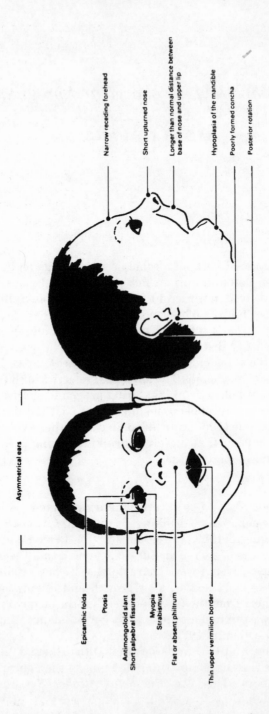

Figure 4.1 Features of the Fetal Alcohol Syndrome.

joint and heart abnormalities, microcephaly and fine motor dysfunction. The distinctive facial characteristics, again noted, included asymmetrical ears, receding chin and forehead and upturned nose. These are illustrated by Figure 4.1.

The original description of the Fetal Alcohol Syndrome was based on only eleven cases examined in Seattle by Ulleland. Relatively little was known about the possible causes of the children's unusual appearances, even though alcohol abuse was evident among the mothers of these children. The syndrome was initially related only to heavy or dependent alcohol consumption. In spite of this, alarm about the adverse effects of alcohol consumption during pregnancy has subsequently spread to include low and moderate drinking (e.g. United States Surgeon General 1981; Dorris 1989). Concern about the possible impact of maternal drinking during pregnancy stimulated a considerable amount of research. It is not possible to review this comprehensively in this short chapter. Even so a selective and critical overview is presented, together with evidence related to the effects of the use of tobacco and other drugs by pregnant women.

Four major US studies have been described by Streissguth et al. (1987). In addition, more detailed reviews have been produced by Rosett and Wiener (1984), by Plant (1985), and by Plant and Plant (1992). The results of research in this field are exemplified by a Scottish study (Plant 1985). This investigation involved a prospective study of 1,008 pregnant women attending a clinic in Edinburgh. These women were initially examined when three months pregnant. Three hundred were also reinterviewed during the thirty-fourth week of their pregnancy. Information about the eventual outcome of pregnancy was elicited from 970 cases, of which 929 produced live births. Because the aetiology of birth defects is complex, data were obtained about a wide range of factors. These included the use and misuse of alcohol, tobacco and prescribed and illicit drugs as well as biographical traits, diet, health and previous obstetric history. The results of this study typify the conclusions of an accumulating body of evidence. First, it was evident that pregnant women who consumed ten units of alcohol on a single drinking occasion were more likely than either lighter drinkers or abstainers to produce offspring with birth defects. Second the results indicated that lower levels of alcohol consumption did not appear to cause foetal damage. The relative influence of a number of factors on birth damage was examined. This supported the conclusion that alcohol consumption has less of an impact than variables such as mother's socioeconomic status and age, previous obstetric history, maternal diet, tobacco smoking and use of both illicit and prescribed drugs. These results closely resembled those from other studies, such as a comparable US investigation conducted in Boston (Hingson et al. 1982; Rosett et al. 1983).

A more recent Scottish study has been described by Forrest et al.
(1991). Initial findings from this study were reported in 1988 (Sulaiman
et al.). This investigation, conducted in Dundee, monitored both the
alcohol use of pregnant women and the development of their offspring
up to eighteen months. This indicated that no evidence of birth defects
were evident among children whose mothers had consumed at least 100
grams of absolute alcohol per week. The authors concluded that pregnant women should consume no more than eight units of alcohol per
week. This study produced results consistent with those described
earlier by other researchers. Available evidence supports the view that
'low' levels of alcohol consumption are unlikely to harm foetal development, but that heavy maternal drinking may be damaging to the foetus.

TOBACCO

The effects of tobacco smoking by pregnant women are well documented.
In the UK, the USA and a number of other countries, tobacco use has been
declining in recent decades. It is also inversely associated with socioeconomic status in the UK, the USA and elsewhere.

Smoking by pregnant women is associated with spontaneous abortion, placental abnormalities, bleeding during pregnancy, increases in
foetal and neonatal abnormality and reduced birth weight. The greater
the number of cigarettes smoked, the greater the risk of perinatal death,
mostly due to complications in labour such as placenta praevia or
prematurity, with the most immediate cause of foetal death being anoxia
(Royal College of Physicians 1986; Froggatt 1988). In addition maternal
exposure to the cigarette fumes of others ('passive smoking') is also
associated with reduced birth weight (Martin and Bracken 1986; Rubin
et al. 1986). Evidence also suggests that women who give up smoking
during pregnancy produce babies with more normal birthweight than
do those who continue to smoke (Sexton and Habel 1984; Macarthur,
Newton and Knox 1987).

ILLICIT AND PRESCRIBED DRUGS

The effects of maternal heroin dependence on foetal development have
been vividly described by Rosenbaum (1981). She reported that the
children of such women were frequently born premature and of low birth
weight. Some exhibited drug withdrawal symptoms. Heavy illicit drug
use is often associated with social disadvantage and with the use of a
wide range of drugs, both legal and illegal. Untreated opiate dependence
among pregnant women is linked with high rates of birth defects and
abortion. However, counselling and support during pregnancy, together
with a maintenance regime of methadone in low doses, has been shown
to improve pregnancy outcome (Finnegan 1982).

The use of crack (a smokeable form of cocaine) has been associated with spontaneous abortion, premature births, foetal death and birth abnormalities, some of which resemble those described in relation to the Fetal Alcohol Syndrome (Revkin 1989). Jabez (1990) has noted that maternal crack use may produce physical damage in the baby such as reduced head circumference with accompanying neurological damage, extra digits and missing limbs. The babies are often also irritable, tremulous and likely to cry much more than normal. Shapiro (1989) has reported that in a good environment most of the effects of crack exposure in pregnancy are not serious and fade soon after birth. However, if the baby continues to live in a drug-using environment the prognosis is poor. (Revkin 1989). The most common problem both for the drug-using mother and her foetus is the irregularity of supply. The damage caused by the continuous cycle of overdose and withdrawal with the resulting oxygen deprivation to the foetus may well be the most damaging factor to foetal health.

Many women use alcohol and/or tobacco, prescribed or illicit drugs during pregnancy. As noted by Whittle and Hanrettey (1987) and Rubin (1987) some prescribed drugs, such as oral anticoagulants, anticonvulsants, some antibiotics and some hormones carry risks if taken during pregnancy. The pregnant woman should always notify her family doctor if she is taking any medication. The dangers of drug use during pregnancy have been increased by the advent of HIV infection. This has sometimes been spread by sharing infected injecting equipment. HIV antibodies have been passed to the foetus by the infected mother. Fortunately, paediatric HIV infection does not inevitably lead to antibody retention or the development of AIDS (Curran et al. 1989, Strang and Stimson 1990). However, only time will tell whether these children are at greater risk from other immunological problems as they get older.

POLYDRUG USE

Women who drink heavily are often also heavy users of tobacco and prescribed or illicit drugs (Plant and Plant 1992). The development of the human foetus may be harmed by exposure to a variety of chemicals (Elkington 1986). The risk of spontaneous abortion may also be dramatically increased.

CONCLUSIONS

There is no doubt that the use, especially the heavy or dependent use, of psychoactive drugs by pregnant women may harm the developing foetus. While a minority of pregnant women do use such substances heavily the majority do not. The heavy or abusive use of alcohol and other drugs is often associated with a variety of risk factors, such as poverty, social deprivation and poor health.

It is clear that the use of alcohol, tobacco and illicit and prescribed drugs during pregnancy is best kept minimal or in most instances avoided altogether. Even so, it is concluded that the possible adverse effects of alcohol consumption during pregnancy have sometimes been exaggerated. Trends in tobacco use in some countries are encouraging. Even so, smoking is still commonplace and in some countries is increasing. In addition the use of prescribed drugs during pregnancy appears to be extremely widespread and in many countries the use of illicit drugs is increasing relentlessly.

REFERENCES

Berridge, V. and Edwards, G. (1981) *Opium and the People*, London, Allen Lane.
Christiaens, L. (1961) 'La descendance des alcooliques' (The offspring of alcoholics) *American Pediatrics* 37, 380.
Curran, J.W., Jaffe, H.W., Hardy, A.M., Morgan, W.M., Selick, R.M. and Dondero, T.J. (1989) 'Epidemiology of AIDS and HIV infection in the United States', in Kulstad, R. (ed.) *AIDS* 1988, Washington, American Association for the Advancement of Science, 19–34.
Dorris, M. (1989) *The Broken Cord*, New York, Harper and Row.
Elkington, J. (1986) *The Poisoned Womb,* Harmondsworth, Pelican.
Finnegan, L.P. (1982) 'Outcome of children born to women dependent upon narcotics' in Stimmel, B. (ed.) *The Effects of Maternal Alcohol and Drug Abuse on the Newborn*, New York, Hawthorn Press.
Forrest, F., du V Florey, C., McPherson, F. and Young, J.A. (1991) 'Reported social alcohol consumption during pregnancy and infants' development at eighteen months', *British Medical Journal* 303, 22–6.
Frogatt, P. (1988) *Smoking and Health*, Further Report of the Independent Scientific Committee, London, HMSO.
Haggard, H.W. and Jellinek, F.M. (1942) *Alcohol Explored*, New York, Doubleday.
Hingson, R., Albert, J.J., Day, N., Dooling, E., Kayne, H., Morelock, S., Oppenheimer, E. and Zuckerman, B. (1982) 'Effects of maternal drinking and marijuana use on fetal growth and development', *Pediatrics* 70, 539–46.
Jabez, A. (1990) 'Crack babies', *Nursing Times* 18, 18–19.
Jones, K.L., and Smith, D.W. (1973) 'Recognition of the foetal alcohol syndrome in early infancy', *Lancet* 2, 999–1001.
Lemoine, P., Harronsseau, H., Borteyrou, J.P. and Menure, J.C. (1968) 'Les enfants de parents alcooliques: Anomalies observées à propos 127 cas' *Quest médicine* 25, 476–82.
MacArthur, C., Newton, J.R. and Knox, E.G. (1987) 'Effect of anti-smoking health education on infant size at birth: a randomised control trial', *British Journal of Obstetrics and Gynaecology* 94, 295–300.
Martin, T.R. and Bracken, M.B. (1986) 'Association of low birth weight with passive smoke exposure in pregnancy', *American Journal of Epidemiology* 124, 633–42.
Montague, A. (1965) *Life Before Birth*, New York, Signet, p. 114.
Plant, M.A. and Plant, M.L. (1992) *Risk-Takers: Alcohol, Drugs, Sex and Young People*, London, Tavistock/Routledge (in press).
Plant, M.L. (1985) *Women, Drinking and Pregnancy*, London, Tavistock.
Revkin, A.C. (1989) 'Crack in the cradle', *Discover*, September, 62–9.
Roquette, P.C. (1957) *The Influence of Parental Alcohol Toxicomania on the Physical and Mental Development of Young Children*, MD thesis, University of Paris.
Rosenbaum, M. (1981) *Women on Heroin*, New Brunswick, Rutgers University Press.
Rosett, H.L. and Weiner, L. (1984) *Alcohol and the Fetus*, New York, Oxford University Press.

Rosett, H.L., Weiner, L., Lee, A., Zuckerman, B., Dooling, E. and Oppenheimer, E. (1983) 'Patterns of alcohol consumption and fetal development', *Obstetrics and Gynaecology* 61, 539–46.

Royal College of Physicians (1986) *Health or Smoking?* London, Pitman.

Rubin, P.C. (ed.) (1987) *Prescribing in Pregnancy*, London, British Medical Journal Publications.

Rubin, D.H., Krasilnikoff, P.A., Leventhal, J.M., Weil, B. and Berget, A. (1986) 'Effect of passive smoking on birth weight', *Lancet* 2, 415–17.

Sexton, M. and Habel, J.R. (1984) 'A clinical trial of change in maternal smoking and its effect on birth weight', *Journal of the American Medical Association* 251, 911–15.

Shapiro, H. (1989) 'Crack – the story so far', *Health Education Journal* 48, 140–4.

Strang, J. and Stimson, G.V. (eds) (1990) *AIDS and Drug Misuse*, London, Tavistock/Routledge.

Streissguth, A.P., Martin, D.C., Martin, J.C. and Barr, H.M. (1987) 'The Seattle longitudinal prospective study on alcohol and pregnancy', *Neurobehavioral Toxicology and Teratology* 3, 223–33.

Sulaiman, N.D., Florey, C.V., Taylor, D.J. and Ogston, S.A. (1988) 'Alcohol consumption in Dundee primigravidas and its effects on outcome of pregnancy', *British Medical Journal* 296, 1500–3.

Sullivan, W.C. (1899) 'A note on the influence of maternal inebriety on the offspring', *Journal of Mental Science* 45, 489–505.

Trotter, T. (1913) *An Essay, Medical, Philosophical and Chemical on Drunkenness and its Effects on the Human Body*, Boston, MA, Bradford and Read (Republished 1981, New York, Arno Press).

Ulleland, C. (1972) 'The offspring of alcoholic mothers', *Annals of the New York Academy of Science* 197, 167–9.

Ulleland, C., Wennberg, R.P., Igo, R.P. and Smith, N.J. (1970) 'The offspring of alcoholic mothers', *Pediatric Resident* 4, 474.

United States Surgeon General (1981) 'Advisory on Alcohol and Pregnancy', *Food and Drug Administration Bulletin,* 1, 9–10.

Whittle, M.J. and Hanrettey, K.P. (1987) 'Identifying abnormalities', in Rubin, P.C. (ed.) *Prescribing in Pregnancy*, London, British Medical Journal, 8–18.

5. *Alcohol, drugs and sexual behaviour*

RUTH MORGAN THOMAS

Alcohol and psychoactive drugs have long been acknowledged to have an impact on social behaviour. Their use, particularly that of alcohol, has become an integral part of most social situations. In addition, the use of alcohol and other psychoactive drugs is often viewed as a sign of maturity and sociability. Within peer groups, those not participating in such recreational drug use are often viewed with suspicion and are subject to peer pressure.

Social contact is a precursor to sexual activity. The use of alcohol and other psychoactive drugs is frequently associated with sexual behaviour. This association has arisen for various reasons, the first of these being the cultural and social connections between the use of recreational drugs and sexual encounters. Establishments such as singles bars, gay bars and sex industry bars have a clear and unambiguous sexual function, but many other licensed premises also, although less blatantly, serve a similar function. Licensed premises or parties where alcohol and other drugs are consumed are often where people mingle and meet new (and old) sexual contacts (Plant 1990, Morgan Thomas 1990). Any such connection may be due to social norms rather than anything more sinister. Second, many recreational drugs have, and are widely believed to have, an impact on sexual arousal and performance and are used in that knowledge or belief to enhance sexual experiences. There is, in addition, the concept of *disinhibition* in relation to psychoactive drugs. This refers to the supposed influence of alcohol, cannabis, cocaine, Ecstasy, amphetamines and a number of other drugs in reducing a person's usual inhibitions (Room and Collins 1983). Alcohol has long been regarded as providing 'Dutch courage' and Longmans Dictionary of Contemporary English (1978) uses drinking as an example of the usage of the word inhibition: 'She gets rid of her inhibitions when she's drunk two or three glasses of wine' (p. 575).

Interestingly enough, to date it has been the female who is most often perceived as being affected. 'Wine-drinking by women was punishable by death in early Rome because it was linked to adultery. It was feared that if a woman opened herself to one male vice, drinking alcohol, she might open herself to another, sexual promiscuity' (Ridlon 1988, pp. 27–8). In addition to this are the complex gender power dynamics at play in social contact, especially in encounters which have a potential for sexual contact. Females are frequently in a difficult bargaining position in relation to sexual encounters.

> Alcohol may be a symbolic instrument of courtship or an agent of physical incapacitation that enables men to take sexual advantage of them ... Alcohol increases women's subjective sexual arousal, but this increased desire does not necessarily lead to initiation of sex. A woman's intoxication might, however, increase the likelihood that she will be seen by a male partner as sexually available. Liberal sexual habits are correlated with liberal drinking habits, but an understanding of the causal order underlying this relationship is elusive (Leigh 1990, p. 141).

With the advent of HIV/AIDS, this known connection between psychoactive drug use and its influence on sexuality has increased concern about the potential role which psychoactive drug use, apart from the obvious risk of sharing injecting equipment, may play in HIV transmission. HIV infection is sexually transmitted. It is passed on through body fluids such as blood, semen and vaginal fluids. It is transmissible man to man, man to woman, woman to man and woman to woman through penetrative sexual contact without protection or when body fluids are allowed to enter the body. Central to this concern is the potential role that recreational drugs may play through their disinhibiting effects. Past research has shown that intoxicating substances, alcohol most commonly, have had a critical role in many unplanned pregnancies and cases of sexually transmitted diseases where people have not taken adequate precautions to protect themselves (Plant and Plant 1992). Obviously there is concern that safer sex guidelines, which are similar to the precautionary measures which should have been complied with to avoid sexually transmitted diseases and unwanted pregnancies, will not in fact be followed and that psychoactive drugs will play a role in this.

There have been few studies which have examined the role of psychoactive drug use in relation to sexual behaviour, although interest has increased with the advent of HIV/AIDS and the realisation of its potential role in transmission of the virus.

In a Scottish study of young people who married while in their teens it was revealed that fifty-eight per cent of males and forty-eight per cent of females had consumed alcohol immediately before their first sexual experiences. Those who had consumed alcohol were significantly less

likely to have used any form of contraception than those who had not
had any alcohol, i.e. thirteen and fifty-seven per cent for males and
twenty-four and sixty-eight per cent for females respectively (Robertson
and Plant 1988). Another Scottish study of young people in Lothian
revealed that both males and females who reported combining alcohol
consumption with sexual activity were seven times less likely than other
respondents to use condoms for vaginal intercourse, although alcohol
consumption levels overall were not related to self reported condom use.
Females in this study who reported adverse alcohol-related consequences were more likely to report their own sexual behaviour as 'risky'.
Males who had adverse alcohol-related consequences reported having
had more sexual partners in the preceding year than did other males.
The authors noted that the vast majority of respondents in this study
reported having had only one sexual partner in the preceding twelve
months. However, serial monogamy is no protection from the virus. In
order to establish the risk of HIV in full, the sexual history of both
partners would need to be taken (Bagnall, Plant and Warwick 1990).

The findings of both the above studies, neither of which focused
primarily on HIV/AIDS, would indicate that there is cause for concern with
regard to alcohol consumption and potential HIV transmission in general. However, it is necessary to gather more detailed information
relating to specific sexual behaviour and precise patterns of psychoactive
drug use before, during and after both new and continuing sexual
contacts before any conclusions can be drawn about the existence of a
causal relationship. In a study conducted in Edinburgh into HIV/AIDS-re-
lated risks in the sex industry, levels of alcohol, psychoactive drug use
and commercial and non commercial sexual activity were examined.
Both male and female sex workers reported high levels of alcohol
consumption and psychoactive drug use. More than seventy-five per cent
of both males and females reported at least sometimes drinking while
working and the majority had also used illicit drugs while working. In
addition the sex workers also reported that over fifty per cent of their
clients were under the influence of alcohol and that they estimated that
almost a third of their clients were under the influence of illicit drugs.
These findings reflect the fact that many of the respondents in this study
contacted clients in licensed premises. Despite the high levels of alcohol
and psychoactive drugs used by this study group the researchers could
find no direct association between sex workers' levels of alcohol consumption or the use of any illicit drugs and self-reported condom use with
clients. (Plant, Plant and Morgan Thomas 1990; Morgan Thomas 1990).
Levels of condom use for penetrative sex among this particular study
group were lower than those recorded by other similar studies. However,
the estimates given by the sex workers were partially validated by the
data obtained from the client study group. The level of condom use

reported by sex workers was 62.9 per cent and that of clients was 61.8 per cent. Among the clients, levels of alcohol consumption were also high, and over three quarters of the study group reported that they at least sometimes consumed alcohol while contacting sex workers. Over forty per cent reported it as the norm. In addition 29.5 per cent of the clients interviewed reported at least sometimes using illicit drugs while contacting sex workers. Over a third of the clients interviewed reported at least sometimes actively seeking unprotected penetrative sex during their contact with sex workers. Among male clients of female sex workers no significant associations between levels of alcohol consumption or psychoactive drug use and self-reported condom use could be found. However, amongst male clients of male sex workers, there was an inverse relationship between alcohol consumption and condom use for penetrative anal intercourse. (Morgan Thomas, Plant and Plant 1990). Condom use with non commercial partners of both sex workers and clients was low; however, no association was found between alcohol consumption or illicit drug use and self-reported condom use.

Outside Scotland, HIV/AIDS-related studies examining the relationships between sexual behaviour and psychoactive drug use have produced conflicting results (Plant and Plant 1992). A study carried out in San Francisco among a cohort of gay men initially found that 'high-risk' sexual activity was associated with the use of alcohol and other psychoactive drugs (Stall et al. 1986; Stall 1988; Stall and Ostrow 1989). However, a similar cohort study conducted in England and Wales actually found that men who had not consumed alcohol immediately prior to sexual contact had a higher incidence of 'high-risk' activities (Weatherburn 1990). Within the England and Wales study, no significant association could be found between levels of alcohol consumption and illicit drug use and 'high-risk' activities. A survey of teenagers in Massachusetts found that heavier drinkers and cannabis users were 2.8 and 1.9 times less likely to report condom use during penetrative sex. Among those who were drinkers or cannabis users sixteen per cent reported using condoms less after drinking and twenty-nine per cent reported using condoms less after using cannabis (Hingson, Strunin and Berlin 1990; Hingson et al. 1990). In a study carried out among young people in Bristol sixty-four per cent of males and fifty per cent of females reported that they were less likely to use condoms if they had been drinking. In addition most of the respondents reported that sex was more pleasurable after drinking and that they had fewer inhibitions (Ford 1990).

All of the studies cited above and many others besides indicate that there is indeed a relationship between alcohol and psychoactive drug use and sexual behaviour. What eludes us at present is exactly what that relationship is and how it may impact on HIV transmission. Among those who are well informed, highly motivated and who view themselves as

potentially at risk from HIV there is a high level of compliance with safer
sex guidelines, and alcohol or psychoactive drug use does not appear to
have a significant impact on this. However, sex workers have not carried
safe sex practices into their non-commercial relationships (e.g. Day and
Ward 1990). Within general population studies, where participants may
not seriously consider themselves at risk of HIV through sexual transmission, there does not appear to be a high compliance with safer sex
guidelines. This would appear to be compounded even further when
alcohol or other psychoactive drugs are involved.

As indicated in Chapters 8 and 9, past alcohol and drug education has
produced little impact on behaviour. Health education has also had little
effect in relation to unwanted pregnancies and sexually transmitted
diseases. It is clear that the identification of 'risk' in itself is not enough
to alter people's behaviour dramatically. As noted by Plant and Plant
(1992) people frequently fail to perceive risks as relevant to themselves:
'It won't happen to me'.

Alongside examining the possible disinhibiting effects of psychoactive
drugs must also come an examination of what inhibits the practice of
safer sex. Foremost amongst such limiting factors is the denial of risk,
which would seem to be accentuated under the influence of psychoactive
drugs.

Among those who perceive themselves to be at risk of HIV infection
through sexual transmission, there has been a much higher acceptance
of safe sex guidelines, primarily among gay men and sex workers.
However, as seen most clearly among sex workers in situations where
they perceive the risks to be less or consider them worth taking in order
not to threaten a relationship, safe sex guidelines are often abandoned.
Too few people outside the formally identified 'high-risk groups' appear
to be taking the threat of HIV seriously. In part, this must be blamed on
the health education campaigns which appeared to single out people
within these groups as being at risk. Much of the work now having to be
carried out is attempting to redress that balance in order to persuade
everyone that they may be at risk if they have been sexually active
without practising safe sex outside a guaranteed lifelong monogamous
relationship (where neither partner has had any 'high-risk' sexual
contact with anyone one prior to that relationship). It is unrealistic to
expect that the majority of people will become celibate or maintain only
one sexual partner throughout their lives. Condoms and non-penetrative
sex have become the primary defence against HIV, and yet they have not
been universally accepted. Condoms are still viewed in a negative light
by many people. Non-penetrative sex is often not viewed as a serious
alternative in a society in which, unless penetration occurs, one has not
really 'done it'.

Regrettably the disinhibiting effects of psychoactive drugs do not appear to have a positive impact on our ability to talk about sex and sexuality or to explore safer alternatives to unprotected penetration. Such drugs would indeed appear to have a negative impact in relation to being careful. Given the potential harm that may be caused in relation to HIV transmission through this, it is essential that the relationship between sexual behaviour and psychoactive drug use be examined in greater detail alongside other factors such as the use of condoms and the disinhibition caused by sexual arousal itself which may influence behaviour. The relative 'bargaining positions' of the participants in sexual activity must be taken into account.

In conclusion, sexual behaviour is often linked with the use of alcohol and other drugs. Even so, this connection is complex and available evidence is conflicting. Sexual activity and psychoactive drug use are connected for a variety for reasons. Even so the precise nature of any cause-and-effect relationship has not yet been clarified.

REFERENCES

Bagnall, G., Plant, M.A. and Warwick, W. (1990) 'Alcohol, drugs and AIDS-related risks: results from a prospective study', *AIDS Care* 2, 309–17.

Day, S. and Ward, S. (1990) 'The Praed Street Project: A cohort of prostitute women in London', in Plant, M.A. (ed.), *AIDS, Drugs and Prostitution*, London, Tavistock/Routledge, 61–75.

Ford, N. (1990) *Psychoactive Drug Use, Sexual Activity and AIDS Awareness of Young People in Bristol*, Institute of Population Studies, University of Exeter.

Hingson, R., Strunin, L. and Berlin, B. (1990) 'Changes in knowledge and behaviours amongst adolescents, Massachusetts, Statewide Surveys 1986–1988', *Paediatrics* 85, 24–9.

Hingson, R. Strunin, L., Berlin, B. and Heeren, T. (1990) 'Beliefs about AIDS, use of alcohol, drugs and unprotected sex amongst Massachusetts adolescents', *American Journal of Public Health* 80, 295–9.

Leigh, B.C. (1990) '"Venus gets in my thinking": Drinking and female sexuality in the age of AIDS', *Journal of Substance Abuse* 2, 129–45.

Morgan Thomas, R. (1990) 'AIDS risks, alcohol, drugs and the sex industry: a Scottish study', in Plant, M.A. (ed.) *AIDS Drugs and Prostitution*, London, Tavistock/Routledge, 88–108.

Morgan Thomas, R., Plant, M.A. and Plant, M.L. (1990) 'Alcohol, AIDS risks and sex industry clients: results from a Scottish study', *Drug and Alcohol Dependence* 26, 265–9.

Plant, M.A. (1990) 'Alcohol, sex and AIDS', *Alcohol and Alcoholism* 29, 293–301.

Plant, M.A. and Plant, M.L. (1992) *Risk-Takers: Alcohol, drugs, sex and youth*, London, Tavistock/Routledge.

Plant, M.L. and Plant, M.A. and Morgan Thomas, R. (1990) 'Alcohol, AIDS risks and commercial sex: some preliminary results from a Scottish study', *Drug and Alcohol Dependence* 25, 51–5.

Ridlon, F.V.C. (1988) *A Fallen Angel: The Status Insularity of the Female Alcoholic*, London, Bricknell University Press.

Robertson, J.A. and Plant, M.A. (1988) 'Alcohol, sex and risks of HIV infection', *Drug and Alcohol Dependence* 22, 75–8.

Room, R. and Collins, G. (eds) (1983) *Alcohol and Disinhibition: Nature and Meaning of the Link*, Washington, DC, NIAAA, Research Monograph 12, US Department of Health and Human Services.

Stall, R. (1988) 'The prevention of HIV infection associated with drugs and alcohol use during sexual activity', in Siegel, L. (ed) *AIDS and Substance Abuse*, New York, Harrington Park Press, 73–88.

Stall, R. McKusick, L., Wiley, J. et al. (1986) 'Alcohol and drug use during sexual activity and compliance with safe sex guidelines for AIDS: The AIDS Behaviorial Research Project', *Health Education Quarterly* 13, 359–71.

Stall, R. and Ostrow, D.A. (1989) 'Intravenous drug use, the combination of drugs and sexual activity and HIV infection among gay and bisexual men: The San Francisco Men's Health Study', *Journal of Drug Issues* 19, 57–73.

Weatherburn, P. (1990) personal communication.

6. HIV infection and AIDS: epidemiology and public health aspects

DERMOT KENNEDY, JOHN EMSLIE AND DAVID GOLDBERG

THE GLOBAL PERSPECTIVE

In June 1981, the first cases of an illness subsequently defined as Acquired Immune Deficiency Syndrome (AIDS) were reported in the USA. Three years later a retrovirus now known as Human Immunodeficiency Virus (HIV) was recognised as the principal transmissible agent in the development of AIDS. Since then, all major areas of the world have come to encounter AIDS. As of 1 July 1991, the World Health Organization (WHO) has received reports of 371,802 AIDS cases, from 162 countries, with USA alone accounting for 179,136 of these; a further twenty countries reported 'zero cases' (World Health Organization 1991a). The WHO estimates that globally more than one million adults and half-a-million children have developed AIDS since the start of the pandemic.

GLOBAL FORECASTS

AIDS represents the end-stage of infection with HIV, mainly HIV-1, and takes an average of eight to ten years to develop. Current AIDS cases reflect HIV infection acquired about a decade ago, while HIV infections transmitted now may not manifest as AIDS until the year 2000 and beyond. WHO experts estimate that by mid-1991, some eight to ten million adults and one million children worldwide have been infected by HIV. However, in the past three years alone, an estimated three million new infections have occurred, mostly in Africa, Asia and Central/South America.

Revised WHO estimates now predict that some forty million adults and children will be infected with HIV and some ten million adults will develop AIDS by the year 2000. About ninety per cent are expected to be in 'developing countries' where many children will be orphaned and many elderly left without support. Dr Jonathan Mann has described HIV

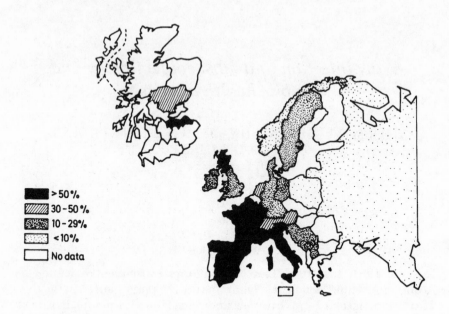

>50%
30-50%
10-29%
<10%
No data

Figure 6.1 The highest rates of HIV infection recorded among intravenous drug users for selected European countries.

infection as the world's first truly global epidemic requiring a truly global strategy in response.

REGIONAL PATTERNS OF HIV SPREAD

WHO has characterised into three main patterns the distinctive regional differences observed so far.

Pattern I regions (North America, Western Europe and Australasia) encountered extensive HIV-1 spread between the mid-1970s and mid-1980s. Initially, most AIDS cases arose from sexual intercourse between men, although injecting drug-use was important in certain areas (e.g. east-coast USA, Spain, Italy, Scotland). Increasingly, new HIV-1 infections involve heterosexual men and women, but overall, to date, male cases predominate.

In *Pattern II* regions (typically sub-Saharan Africa), extensive HIV-1 spread probably started in the 1970s, but heterosexual transmission has predominated from the outset. Numbers of affected males and females are approximately equal, with mother-to-child 'vertical transfer' an important derivative. A mixed *Pattern I/II* situation is developing in Central/South America.

In *Pattern III* regions (Eastern Europe and Asia), HIV-1 appeared only

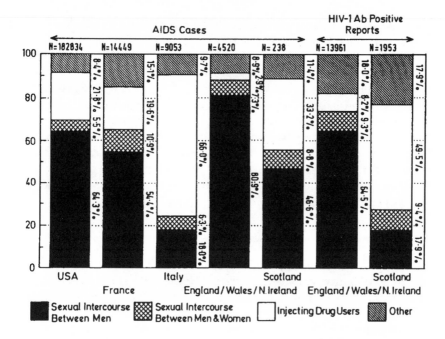

Figure 6.2 A comparison of transmission categories for AIDS cases and HIV-1 Ab positive reports among selected European countries and the USA (June 1991).

recently, thus more time must elapse before any predominant mode of spread manifests.

Already, however, focal spread has occurred under particular circumstances: in children's institutions (Romania and the Soviet Union) due to inadequacies of hygiene and sterilisation; among intravenous drug users (parts of India); and among prostitutes (Thailand).

Elsewhere, potential exists for dispersal of HIV-1; for example, large numbers of intravenous drug users are known to exist in Poland and Yugoslavia where, as yet, HIV has gained only limited access.

EXPERIENCE OF SUBSTANCE MISUSE AND HIV-1 INFECTION

In the USA, staff at the Centers for Disease Control (CDS) describe two self-sustaining epidemics; one based upon male-to-male sexual transmission and the other on substance misuse. These epidemics are nearly independent, differ in time trends and affect different population groups.

Homosexual transmission manifests as geographically diffuse and involves mostly whites with, recently, a decreasing rate of incidence of AIDS cases. Transmission due to injecting drug-use is concentrated on the east coast and predominantly involves blacks or Hispanics, and the increase in AIDS cases continues. With the advent of 'crack cocaine', increased rates of infection due to sexual activity by crack users have occurred.

Heterosexual and perinatal patterns of transmission closely resemble the drug-related pattern, as do patterns for other surveyed groups (e.g. military recruits, Job Corps students, child-bearing women, non-homosexual sexually transmitted disease patients, and tuberculosis patients). Injecting drug-use is perceived therefore as the primary driving force behind an increasing part of the HIV-1 epidemic in the USA. Efforts to prevent drug misuse and associated HIV transmission are seen to be fundamental to achieving control of HIV spread, both directly and indirectly (Dondero et al. 1991).

HIV INFECTION AND INJECTING DRUG-USE IN SCOTLAND AND EUROPE

From a population of approximately 5.1 million, Scotland has an estimated 20,000 intravenous drug users (McClelland 1990) – a rate of 392 per 100,000 population. By contrast, the rest of the UK has some 90,000 intravenous drug users from a population of 52.1 million, or 173 per 100,000. Scotland compares unfavourably by rate with estimates for several other European countries; Poland 236, France 179, Italy 174, Denmark 157, Sweden 141 and the Netherlands 117. In Edinburgh and Dundee, Scotland also has rates of HIV-1 infection which approach the highest rates found in parts of Italy, Spain and France. This is elaborated by Figure 6.1 in which unless otherwise stated, figures on prevalence of drug use and HIV among drug users are from Brenner, Hernando-Briangos and Goos (1991).

Wide variations in rates of HIV-1 infection exist geographically within European countries, for example thirty per cent in Amsterdam compared to 3.6 per cent in Arnhem. Scotland compared with the rest of the UK accounts for one tenth of the population, one twentieth of the AIDS cases but one seventh of HIV-infected persons recorded (mid-1991). The dynamics of the epidemic differ not only between Scotland, the rest of the UK and several other countries (as shown by Figure 6.2), but also between parts of Scotland. Within the UK, the three principal Scottish conurbations continue to face the highest rates of drug-associated HIV infections per million population: Edinburgh 786, Dundee 487 and Glasgow 147, compared with 60 for London as a whole.

SCOTLAND: THE CONTRAST BETWEEN EAST AND WEST

Rates differ markedly between the east and the west of Scotland which are only some 70–100 kilometres apart. Glasgow in the west is Scotland's largest city and has the largest population of intravenous drug users, currently estimated at about 9,500 (Frischer et al. 1991). However, the rate of HIV-1 infection has never exceeded seven per cent during the period 1985 to early 1991. A community-wide study in 1990 of 500 IDUs yielded an overall prevalence of 1.4 per cent (Haw et al. 1991). By contrast, in the east, rates of sixty-four per cent (Skidmore et al. 1991) in Edinburgh (2,500 to 4,000 intravenous drug users) and thirty-nine per cent (Urquhart et al. 1987) in Dundee (1,500 to 2,000) have been recorded. Regrettably, to date these Scottish east/west differences have not been explained adequately, but some interesting indicators are available.

A small study in 1986 (Bucknall, Robertson and Wiggins 1986) compared general-practice experiences of intravenous drug users' risk-behaviour in Edinburgh and Glasgow. This indicated that Edinburgh drug injectors had shared equipment more frequently and with more individuals than had drug injectors in Glasgow. Mean sharing-events per month were 46 and 15.4 respectively and mean persons-sharing per month were 14.2 and 7.1.

Ethnographic studies undertaken in Edinburgh suggested that circumstances may have existed in the early- to mid-1980s which facilitated access by HIV-1 to groups of susceptible drug injectors. Some individuals may have been in a biological state of high infectivity. Inadequate disinfection of equipment between uses could have contributed to rapid and extensive dispersal of HIV-1 from quite a small number of infected individuals. Thereafter, the severity of the problem in Edinburgh was recognised and a public health response to it initiated. Anecdotal evidence about the concurrent 'drug scene' in Glasgow implies that similar phenomena did exist in the west but were considerably less prevalent. Although Glasgow has many more drug users than Edinburgh, intravenous drug users form more geographically distinct groups than in the east. Possibly, these characteristics served to minimise HIV-1 spread in Glasgow.

HIV SPREAD OUTSIDE THE DRUG INJECTING POPULATION IN SCOTLAND

The majority of drug injectors are young (95.2 per cent are aged between fifteen and thirty-nine years) and heterosexual (Communicable Diseases (Scotland) Weekly Report 1991); a group likely to fuel the spread of HIV into the wider heterosexual community. To monitor this in Scotland, a programme of surveys has recently been introduced, following on a study of pregnant women in Edinburgh and Dundee which showed an HIV-1 prevalence of 2.5 per thousand for the period November 1988 to July 1990 (Goldberg, MacKinnon et al. 1992). Since eighteen per cent of the HIV-Ab positive women were neither intravenous drug users nor sexual partners of men considered to be 'at high risk of infection', the results indicate that HIV-1 has begun already to infiltrate the general, 'low-risk' populations.

A series of unlinked, anonymous testing (UAT) studies has been initiated and includes HIV-testing of (1) genito-urinary clinic attenders; (2) hospital inpatient and outpatient, along with general practice, attenders aged between sixteen and forty-nine years; and (3) child-bearing women. For 1990, the third group yielded prevalence rates which range from zero per cent in the west of Scotland to 0.25 per cent in Edinburgh (Tappin et al. 1991). In due course, results gleaned from the other study groups are expected to provide similar valuable information about HIV-1 prevalence in young men as well as men and women at high risk.

The first prevalence study of HIV-1 infection among prisoners in the UK was conducted in Edinburgh in August 1991. Unlike some European countries, the UK does not have any mechanism to collect data routinely from such a source. With prostitutes also, accurate data on the prevalence of HIV is not available in the UK, but, of 120 such persons HIV-tested in Scotland during 1989 and 1990, only one – an intravenous drug user – proved to be positive (Goldberg, Emslie et al. 1992).

Effective monitoring of the spread of HIV is a prerequisite for public health intervention and control, both in Scotland and elsewhere. Accurate information is needed for the National Health Service (NHS) in Scotland (1) to plan resource-allocation for the care of HIV-infected persons; (2) to educate this population about relevant ways to prevent further spread of HIV; and (3) to evaluate the efficacy of interventive measures to reduce dispersal of HIV. Altogether, these might be called a '3E programme' of Economics, Education and Evaluation. Meanwhile, existing HIV-1 infections are expected to yield increasing numbers of AIDS cases each year at least until the mid- to late 1990s. For Scotland, a cumulative total of 950 cases of AIDS is predicted by the end of 1993 (McClelland 1990).

THE NATURE OF HIV RISK-TAKING BEHAVIOUR IN DRUG USERS

Drug users may become infected with HIV in one of two ways: by the sharing of injecting equipment, or by sexual intercourse, either heterosexual or homosexual. Sexual transmission is often underestimated as a means of initiating infection in intravenous drug users, unlike the situation with non-drug-injectors. However, American experience of the 'crack' epidemic emphasises the increasing importance of this phenomenon. Drugs such as cocaine or amphetamines tend to enhance the degree and randomness of sexual activity while increasing indifference to risk-taking. Moss (1990) has suggested that drug users in the USA may now be infected as commonly by the sexual route as by the intravenous one.

For most drug users in the UK the major risk for transmission remains the sharing of equipment. Behavioural factors which are most commonly associated with HIV infection include the duration of injecting drug-use, the frequency of injecting and of sharing and the total number of partners involved in each sharing event (Chaisson et al. 1987). Sharing with strangers is also important. This may occur in 'shooting galleries' where drugs and equipment are commercially supplied and used on the premises, or when 'house works' are lent by dealers to their customers (Marmor et al. 1987). The use of intravenous cocaine has now become an important risk factor in the USA (Sterk 1988) and justifies further the continuing need to monitor closely for the presence of this drug in the UK.

The risk of infection also relates to the extent of spread within a drug-using community. Sometimes, this can develop very rapidly, as in Edinburgh in 1983/4 (Robertson et al. 1986; Peutherer et al. 1985) and, more ominously, in Bangkok in 1988. Once seroprevalence rates reach a threshold of perhaps ten to fifteen per cent, spread of infection seems to accelerate.

As well as behaviour, there may be other biological or virological variables which enhance the spread of HIV. For example, HIV infected individuals are more infectious (1) during the early 'window period', after infection is initiated but before any antibody appears; and (2) with functional deterioration of the immune system, especially when the CD4 lymphocyte count declines below 300 cells per cubic millimetre.

The role of co-factors in facilitating either the acquisition or progression of HIV-1 infection is debatable. Sexual acquisition seems related to some chronic genital infections, such as chancroid or syphilis, which are increasing markedly among the inhabitants of the inner cities of the USA. Once established, HIV disease appears to progress more rapidly in older than in younger persons, which favours younger drug injectors over older homosexual or bisexual males. However, those who continue to inject seem to incur more rapid deterioration than those who have stopped (Des Jarlais et al. 1987). More controversial still is the contention that certain other chronic infections may also accelerate HIV disease.

MAJOR TRANSMISSIBLE INFECTIONS ASSOCIATED WITH INJECTING DRUG-USE

Hepatitis B virus (HBV) is probably still the most common communicable disease affecting drug injectors. It is a useful and early marker of the extent of sharing in a drug culture. In approximately twenty-five per cent of drug injectors infected with HBV, a clinical illness (hepatitis) develops some four to six months after infection; with those infected with HIV, the appearance of symptoms comes much later. Most HBV-infected people clear their infection asymptomatically, while perhaps five per cent become chronically infected. Sero-surveys of drug injectors have shown an approximately similar prevalence of HBV infection in Edinburgh and in Glasgow, with rates of about seventy to eighty per cent

(Follett et al. 1986). Since immunisation is available for this infection, should not more effort be directed to preventing it among intravenous drug users?

Recently, a newly identified virus able to cause chronic liver disease, Hepatitis C, has been detected at high seroprevalence among drug injectors; for example, in Glasgow about sixty-five per cent (Follett 1991). As yet, the actual scale of infectious threat posed by these seropositives is unknown.

Another human retrovirus, the Human T-Lymphotropic Virus type I (HTLV-I) is associated with neurological and haematological disease. Found in ten to fifteen per cent of drug injectors surveyed in parts of America and Europe, it has been implicated as another possible co-factor for rapid progression of HIV-1 disease.

PUBLIC HEALTH INITIATIVES

Once the scale of the HIV problem in the east of Scotland was appreciated fully, the Scottish Home and Health Department commissioned a special committee of inquiry to consider implications and make recommendations. The resulting 'McClelland Report' of 1986 (Scottish Committee on HIV Infection and Intravenous Drug Misuse) emphasised not only that HIV infection posed greater threat to life than did drug use, but also that prevention of the spread of HIV should have precedence over prevention of drug use. One practical consequence was the establishment, from 1987 onwards, of needle/syringe exchange facilities in thirteen cities within the UK. Special roles in prevention were emphasised for doctors, pharmacists, police, educationalists and outreach drug workers. Subsequently, an extensive publicity campaign was initiated. In 1988 and 1989, the UK government's Advisory Council on the Misuse of Drugs (ACMD) published its report in two parts. Again, the change in strategy underpinning the Council's many recommendations was that all agencies should adopt policies to encourage harm-minimisation by those clients who continued to misuse drugs. It described various ways to maximise contact with users; in particular a wider, though judicious, use of substitute prescribing by both specialists and general practitioners. By these means, drug users could be moved gradually through a hierarchy of behavioural changes towards safer drug use. These reports marked a sea-change in the UK's approach to drug misuse. However, it is too early yet to assess their effect in slowing the spread of HIV, especially since their recommendations, let alone the underlying philosophies, have yet to be accepted fully.

EXCHANGES OF INJECTING EQUIPMENT

These units were initially very controversial and met with considerable public opposition in Scotland. Although the Dundee facility soon closed, that in Edinburgh has had somewhat more success. Glasgow's programme encountered initial hostile picketing, but has expanded very successfully until now there are six facilities, including a prostitutes' drop-in centre (Elliot et al. 1991). In the first half of 1991, no fewer than 1,641 drug injectors made 9,687 visits in order to borrow 84,823 sets of injecting equipment (as well as condoms) and return 106,035; presumably the excess equipment was purchased from pharmacies. In general, contact has facilitated the provision of additional counselling and education on HIV and drug issues to many individuals who were never in touch with services in the past. For a minority of clients, it has led also to onward referral to other agencies.

SUBSTITUTE PRESCRIBING

This issue has created controversy, since in Scotland there is a history of opposition to it. This has been based not only on theoretical grounds, such as the sanctioning and prolongation of drug dependence, but also because of the practical problems of prescribing. Disruptive users with chaotic lifestyles may sell their drugs and could cause legal difficulties for their prescribers. However, considerable evidence has now emerged from Europe and the USA to demonstrate the effectiveness of methadone therapy, in particular, to reduce or eliminate the injection of opiate drugs (Ball et al. 1988; Hubbard et al. 1988; Novick et al. 1990; Robert et al. 1990). Perhaps most importantly, it ensures ongoing contact with a more stable user to allow long-term counselling about drug problems and the value of harm-minimisation.

In 1988, a study of HIV-infected female intravenous drug users in Glasgow revealed that seventy-five per cent were selling sexual services to finance their drug-using habits (Goldberg, Green et al. 1988). This information emphasised the real danger of HIV spreading from this group into the wider heterosexual population. Accordingly, the public health response to this concern was the establishment in May 1988 of a health care drop-in centre for Glasgow street prostitutes. A similar centre for Edinburgh was opened in 1990 (Morgan Thomas 1990).

From evidence on behavioural change that is now beginning to accumulate, it is encouraging to find that drug injectors in Glasgow (Haw et al. 1991) and, particularly in Edinburgh (Skidmore et al. 1990) appear to be adopting a degree of safer drug use. However, in the light of the American and European experience of HIV spread among heterosexuals, it is worrying that intravenous drug users in the main continue to have high levels of unsafe sex (Haw et al. 1991).

REFERENCES

Advisory Council on the Misuse of Drugs (1988) *AIDS and Drug Misuse* Part 1, London, HMSO.

Advisory Council on the Misuse of Drugs (1989) *AIDS and Drug Misuse* Part 2, London, HMSO.

Ball, J.C., Lange, W.R., Myers, C.P. and Friedman, S.R. (1988) 'Reducing the risk of AIDS through methadone maintenance treatment', *Journal of Health and Social Behaviour* 29, 214–66.

Brenner, H., Hernando-Briangos, P. and Goos, C. (1991) *AIDS Among Drug Users in Europe*, Copenhagen, World Health Organization, Regional Office for Europe.

Bucknall, A.B.V., Robertson, J.R. and Wiggins, P. (1986) 'Regional variations in HIV antibody seropositivity in British intravenous drug users', *Lancet* i, 1435–6.

Chaisson, R.E., Moss, A.R., Onishi, R., Osmond, D., and Carlson, J.R. (1987) 'Human immunodeficiency virus infection in heterosexual intravenous drug users in San Francisco', *American Journal of Public Health* 77, 169–72.

Communicable Diseases (Scotland) (1991) *Weekly Report* 25, no. 29 suppl., ANSWER A208.

Des Jarlais, D.C., Friedman, S.R., Marmor, M., Cohen, H. and Mildvan, D. (1987) 'Development of AIDS HIV seroconversion, and potential co-factors for T4 cell loss in a cohort of intravenous drug users', *AIDS* I, 105–11.

Dondero, T.J., Allen, D.M., McCray, E., Gwinn, M., Conway, G.A., Onorato, I.M. and Selik, R.M. (1991) 'Injected drug abuse: the driving force for much of the US HIV epidemic', Abstract no. WC 3356, VIIth International Conference on AIDS, June 1991, Florence, Italy.

Elliot, L., Hardie, A., Cameron, J. and Gruer, L. (1991) 'Expanding service provision at Glagow needle exchanges', *Communicable Diseases (Scotland) Weekly Report* 25, no. 29 suppl., ANSWERS 216.

Follett, E.A.C., McIntyre, A., O'Donnell, B., Clements, G.B. and Desselberger, U. (1986) 'HTLV III antibody in drug abusers in the West of Scotland: the Edinburgh connection', *Lancet* i, 446–7.

Frischer, M., Bloor, M., Finlay, A. et al. (1991) 'A new method of estimating prevalence of injecting drug-use in an urban population: results from a Scottish city', *International Journal of Epidemiology* 204, 21–6.

Frischer, M., Green, S. et al. (1991) 'HIV and injecting drug use in Glasgow: Past, present and future', To be submitted for publication.

Goldberg, D., Emslie, J., Smyth, W., Allardice, G. and Reid, D. (1991) 'A system for surveillance of voluntary HIV testing: results of the first two years, 19891990', *AIDS* (in press).

Goldberg, D., Green, S.T., Kingdom, J., Christie, P. (1988) 'HIV among female drug misusing prostitutes in Greater Glasgow', *Communicable Diseases (Scotland) Weekly Report* 22, no. 12 suppl., ANSWER A48.

Goldberg, D., Mackinnon, H., Smith, R. et al. (1992) 'Prevalence of human immunodeficiency virus among child-bearing women and those undergoing termination of pregnancy', accepted for publication by *British Medical Journal* (in press).

Haw, S., Frischer, M., Covell, R. et al. (1991) 'HIV infection and risk behaviour among injecting drug users in Glasgow', *Communicable Diseases (Scotland) Weekley Report* 25, no. 31 suppl., ANSWER A210.

Hubbard, R.L., Marsden, M.E., Cavanaugh, E., Valley Rachal, J. and Ginsburg, H.M. (1988) 'Role of drug abuse treatment in limiting the spread of AIDS', *Review of Infectious Diseases* 10, 377–83.

Marmor, M., Des Jarlais, D.C., Cohen, H., Friedman, S.R., and Beatrice, S.T. (1987) 'Risk factors for infection with human immunodeficiency virus among intravenous drug abusers in New York City', *AIDS* I, 39–44.

'McClelland Report' (1990) 'Acquired Immune Deficiency Syndrome in Scotland –
    Projections to the end of 1993', Report of a Working Group convened by the
    Chief Medical Officer, Scottish Home and Health Department, 8/90 (027908),
    HMSO Reprographic Unit, Edinburgh.

Morgan Thomas, R. (1990) 'AIDS risks, alcohol, drugs and the sex industry: a
    Scottish study', in Plant, M.A. (ed.), *AIDS, Drugs and Prostitution*, London,
    Tavistock/Routledge, 88–108.

Moss, A.R. (1990) 'Epidemiology of the injecting drug-using population: An
    overview of the US situation in aspects of HIV management in injecting drug
    users', *International Seminar Series*, Colwood House Medical Publications
    (UK) Ltd.

Novick, D.M., Joseph, H., Croxon, T.S., Salsitz, E.A., Wang, G., and Richman,
    B.L. (1989) 'Absence of antibody to HIV in long-term socially rehabilitated
    methadone maintenance patients', *Archives of Internal Medicine* 150 (1) 97–9.

Peutherer, J.J., Edmond, E., Simmonds, P., Dickson, J.D. and Bath, G.E. (1985)
    'HTLV III antibody in Edinburgh drug addicts', *Lancet* ii, 1129–30.

Robert, C.F., Deglon, J.J., Wintsch, J., Martin, J.L., Perrin, L. and Bourquin, M.
    (1990) 'Behavioural changes in intravenous drug users in Geneva: rise and
    fall of HIV infection 1980–1989', *AIDS* 4; 657–60.

Robertson, J.R., Bucknall, A.B.V., Welsby, P.D., Inglis, J.M., Peutherer, J.F.,
    Brettle, R.P. and Roberts, J.K. (1986) 'Epidemic of AIDS related virus (HTLV
    II/LAV) infection among intravenous drug users' (1986) *British Medical
    Journal* 292, 527–30.

Robertson, J.R., Skidmore, C.A. and Roberts, J.K. (1988, 'HIV infection in
    intravenous drug users: a follow-up study indicating changes in risk-taking
    behaviour', *British Journal of Addiction* 83, 337–91.

Sato, P.A., Chin, J. and Mann, J.M. (1989) 'Review of AIDS and HIV Infection:
    global epidemiology and statistics', *AIDS* v, 3, (auppl. 1) 301–7.

Schiidm – The Report of the Scottish Committee on HIV Infection and
    Intravenous Drug Misuse (1986) Scottish Home and Health Department.

Skidmore, C.A., Robertson, J.R., Robertson, A.A., Elton, R.A. (1990) 'After the
    epidemic: follow-up study of HIV seroprevalence and changing patterns of
    drug use', *British Medical Journal* 300, 219–23.

Sterk, C. (1988) 'Cocaine and HIV seropositivity', *Lancet* i; 1052–3.

Tappin, D.M., Girdwood, R.W.A., Follett, E.A.C., Kennedy, R., Brown, A.J.,
    Cockburn, F. (1991) 'Prevalence of maternal HIV infection in Scotland based
    on unlinked anonymous testing of newborn babies', *Lancet* 337, 1565–7.

Urquhart, G.E.D., Scott, S.S., Woodridge, E. et al. (1991) 'Human
    Immunodeficiency Virus (HIV) in intravenous drug abusers in Tayside',
    Communicable Diseases (Scotland) Weekly Report 1919 25, no. 29, Suppl.,
    ANSWER A208.

World Health Organization (1989) *Weekly Epidemiological Record* 64, No. 30,
    229–31, Geneva, World Health Organization.

World Health Organization (1991a) *Weekly Epidemiological Record* 66, No. 27,
    197–8, Geneva, World Health Organization.

World Health Organization (1991b) *The Global HIV/AIDS Situation*, Office of
    Information, Geneva publication No. 74, In Point of Fact series, Geneva,
    World Health Organization.

7. Clinical aspects of HIV/AIDS among drug users

RAY BRETTLE

The Centers for Disease Control (CDC) in Atlanta described a useful clinical classification system which details four stages of HIV infection as shown in Table 7.1.

I	acute infection with seroconversion		
II	asymptomatic infection		
III	persistent generalised lymphadenopathy		
IV	A	constitutional disease	
	B	neurological disease	
	C	immunodeficiency	
		C1	CDC definition of AIDS
		C2	infections outwith definition
	D	tumours in CDC definition of AIDS	
	E	other, e.g. Hodgkins, carcinoma, lymphoid interstitial pneumonia	

Source: Centers for Disease Control 1983 and 1987a

Table 7.1 CDC classification of effects of HIV infection

This system does not assume that every individual progresses through all stages but that, having reached a particular stage, they do not revert to earlier stages. CDC stage IV contains conditions currently used for the definition of AIDS as well as other clinically significant problems which fall short of full-blown AIDS (previously known as AIDS-Related Complex or ARC).

PRIMARY HIV INFECTION

CDC stage I describes a self-limiting illness during the initial infection with HIV. It may mimic glandular fever but seems difficult to identity in drug users.

EARLY MANIFESTATIONS OF HIV INFECTION

Individuals at stage II are well or asymptomatic while those at stage III have enlarged lymph nodes (greater than one centimetre) or 'glands' as well as other troublesome symptoms such as tiredness, lethargy, excessive sweating, aches and pains in muscles or joints.

LATE MANIFESTATIONS OF HIV INFECTION

Individuals at stage IVA complain of the vague constitutional symptoms of stage III but with the addition of unexplained diarrhoea, fever for longer than one month and/or unexplained weight loss of more than ten per cent body weight over the previous six months.

Stage IVB consists of neurological problems such as loss of function in nerves or the spinal cord resulting in weakness or frank paralysis. Patients or relatives may also notice loss of memory, skills such as mental arithmetic and decision-making, or even changes in personality. Frank mental illness, dementia or loss of consciousness can also occur. If no other cause is found, then this is HIV encephalopathy and is one criterion for the diagnosis of full-blown AIDS.

Stage IVC contains infections which occur as a result of immunodeficiency and is divided into two subgroups IVC1 and IVC2. Subgroup IVC1 includes one or more of the twelve infections which formed the basis of the original CDC definition of AIDS. One of the commonest infections is Pneumocystis carinii pneumonia (PCP), which may present as an acute illness with fever, cough and shortness of breath. Such individuals may not look that unwell but they have a history of shortness of breath with only minimal exercise such as ascending one flight of stairs. Stage IVC2 describes infections which are commonly associated with serious HIV infection but were not in the original description of AIDS. Examples are recurrent and invasive salmonellosis, extensive herpes zoster (shingles), recurrent oral thrush or candidiasis and oral hairy leucoplakia (white patches along the tongue's edge).

Stage IVD describes cancers specifically associated with HIV infection such as the skin tumour Kaposi's sarcoma (KS). Lastly, CDC stage IVE is for conditions not yet described or those not yet understood, for instance excessive bruising or bleeding as a consequence of a lack of platelets (HIV-related thrombocytopenia) (Jaffe et al. 1983; Morris et al. 1982; Ratnoff et al. 1983; Savona et al. 1985). This is a relatively benign condition and the commonest symptoms are excessive bruising, epistaxis, menorrhagia, and gingival and rectal bleeding. Major life-threatening haemorrhage is rare.

PROGRESSION FROM HIV TO AIDS

A number of factors may affect progression from early HIV infection to AIDS, including genetic susceptibility, gender, pregnancy, risk activity, co-infection with other viruses, and age. Additional immunosuppression might also be important, such as arises from the use of opiates, stimulation of the immune system via soluble antigens and viruses and the acquisition of differing strains of HIV (Anonymous 1984; Fauci 1987; Hahn et al. 1986; Rivin et al. 1984; Tubaro et al. 1983). A number of co-factors affecting progression have been noted including age, low numbers of CD4 lymphocytes (less than 200 per cubic millimetre suggests that fifty per cent will progress in two years) thrombocytopenic purpura, HIV antigen in serum and rising levels of B-2-microglobulin (Eyster et al. 1987; Gold et al. 1988; Lacey et al. 1988; Lambin et al. 1988; Polk et al. 1987; Winkelstein 1988).

It is possible that the majority of patients will eventually develop AIDS, but the time from HIV infection to the onset of AIDS is variable (Goedert et al. 1986; Kaplan et al. 1987; Marthur-Wagh et al. 1985; Melbye et al. 1986; Taylor et al. 1986). Progression from HIV to AIDS in cohorts of various risk groups with known seroconversion dates occurred at the rate of 0–2 per cent at 2 years, 5–10 per cent at 4 years, 10–25 per cent at 6 years, 30–40 per cent at 8 years and 51 per cent by 10 years (Crovari et al. 1988; Gatell et al. 1990; Lifson et al. 1990; Moss and Bacchetti 1989; Rezza et al. 1989; Rutherford et al. 1990; Vaccher et al. 1988; Zulaica et al. 1988). However among drug users, AIDS cases greatly under-represent serious intravenous drug-use-related HIV disease. In New York and Milan, there has been a rapid increase in both AIDS-related and non-AIDS, narcotic-related deaths; for every AIDS-related death in a drug user, there was one other as a consequence of such conditions as tuberculosis, endocarditis and bacterial pneumonia (Galli et al. 1988; Stoneburner et al. 1989; Weber et al. 1990).

While Kaslow et al. (1989) found no evidence for a role of alcohol or other psychoactive drugs in accelerating the progression of immunodeficiency in HIV seropositive homosexual and bisexual men, there are reports that continued intravenous drug use accelerates immunodeficiency (Des Jarlais et al. 1987; Flegg et al. 1989). There was also a lower probability of disease progression reported in Switzerland among methadone users or ex-users compared to those who continued intravenous drug use (Weber et al. 1990). However, other groups have not found an increased risk for continued intravenous drug use (Robertson et al. 1990; Selwyn et al. 1990; Selwyn et al. 1990).

CLINICAL FEATURES OF DRUG RELATED
HIV AND AIDS

One of the major difficulties is differentiating HIV from drug-use-related problems. For instance, lymphadenopathy may be associated with intra-venous drug use as may fatigue, lethargy and excessive sweating as a consequence of mild withdrawal from opiates (Brettle, Farrell and Strang 1990). Despite these problems there is in fact little variation between the risk groups with regard to the clinical presentation of AIDS. In the USA, conditions such as KS are unusual in the absence of homo-sexuality or bisexuality (Selik, Starcher and Curran 1987). In drug users, KS, cytomegalovirus and chronic cryptosproidiosis are all signifi-cantly less common than for all other risk groups notified with AIDS, while PCP, tuberculosis, oesophageal candidiasis and extrapulmonary cryptococcosis are more common (Selik, Starcher and Curran 1987).

The incidence of tuberculosis is much higher in HIV-infected drug users; in fact in the USA, most patients with AIDS and tuberculosis have been drug users (Handwerger et al. 1987; Sunderma et al. 1986). The former of these studies showed a prevalence of fifteen per cent in drug users with AIDS but only four per cent in other risk groups within a New York hospital. Elsewhere in New York the rate of tuberculosis was four per cent amongst HIV-positive drug users compared to zero per cent in HIV-negative drug users and the thirty-six per cent increase in reported cases of tuberculosis between 1984 and 1986 has been largely ascribed to infection among HIV-positive drug users (Centers for Disease Control 1987b; Selwyn et al. 1989).

Bacteria such as Streptococcus pneumonia and Haemophilus influ-enza are frequent causes of chest infections and bacteraemias in HIV-positive individuals (Simberkoff et al. 1984). The annual incidence of pneumonia for AIDS patients is ten per cent for drug users compared to under two per cent for homosexual males (Polsky et al. 1986; Selwyn et al. 1988b). Intravenous drug use-related HIV patients have a higher incidence of recurrent bacterial infections such as pneumonia; twelve per cent with a mortality of 2.2 per cent compared to three per cent with a mortality of zero per cent in HIV-negative drug users (Selwyn et al. 1988a). Consequently, the mortality from pneumonia in young adults in New York City is rising primarily due to intravenous drug-use-related HIV, and other cities in the USA are showing similar trends (Centers for Disease Control, 1988). The morbidity and mortality of bacterial endo-carditis in HIV-seropositive individuals are also greater than for serone-gative individuals, at twenty-four per cent compared with four per cent (Ruggeri, Sathe and Kapila 1988; Slim et al. 1988). Interestingly, this susceptibility to bacterial infection is not limited to drug users. In Nairobi, HIV-seropositive individuals were five times more likely to suffer a bacteraemia (twenty-six per cent versus six per cent) particularly with Streptococcus pneumoniae and Salmonella typhimurium (Gilks et al. 1990).

The reasons for the increase in bacterial infections in HIV patients are not yet clear, but less use of medical services may be one important factor. Others may be that opiates themselves depress the cough reflex as well as the immune system, and that unsterile drug injection exposes the individual to recurrent episodes of bacterial infection.

Hepatitis B is a frequent infection among injecting drug users, and in Edinburgh ninety-one per cent of HIV seropositives have markers of infection as opposed to fifty-one per cent of seronegative drug users, reflecting the frequency of drug use and the extent of equipment-sharing (Burns et al. 1987). A recently described event is the reactivation of Hepatitis B infection among drug users during the course of HIV infection (Vento et al. 1989).

SURVIVAL AFTER THE DEVELOPMENT OF AIDS

Around fifty per cent of patients with AIDS survive one year but only twenty per cent three years (Rothenberg et al. 1987). It is generally assumed that the survival period for drug users is shorter, but in New York there was no difference between homosexuals and drug users in terms of survival. Injection drug use itself may be an adverse factor, however, since the combination of intravenous drug use and homosexuality did lead to shorter survival and there was a significant interaction between IDU and Pneumocystis carinii pneumonia (PCP) in shortening survival (Rothenberg et al. 1987).

The survival statistics for US drug users may be affected by the poor survival period of women, possibly related to a delay in diagnosis, since sixteen per cent of women die at diagnosis of AIDS compared to eleven per cent of men (Rothenberg et al. 1987). A greater risk of respiratory failure was observed for women with PCP as well as a twofold increase in the mortality compared to a matched group of men (Verdegem, Sattler and Boylen 1988). In New Jersey, for female patients, ninety-five per cent of whom were black and sixty-three per cent drug users, the mean survival was only 14.5 weeks (Kloser, Grigoriu and Kapila 1988). By comparison, one series of twenty-four women, all white and from Rhode Island, suggested improved survival for women since the mean length of survival was nineteen months and only five had PCP (Carpenter et al. 1988). Overall however, the prognosis seems to be poorer for women, since in the New York series the cumulative probability of survival at one year was seventy-five per cent for white males with Kaposi's sarcoma but only thirty-seven per cent for black female drug users with PCP (Rothenberg et al. 1987).

The poor outcome for women and possibly drug users in the USA probably has more to do with access to care rather than an effect of HIV. There are studies demonstrating that US women present late for care and that patients attending an outpatient clinic had a better survival, 70.4 weeks compared to 27.5 weeks for non-attenders (Kloser et al. 1987; Young and Pierce 1990). In Minnesota, two-thirds of women with HIV were detected at neonatal screening rather than being in medical care (Danila et al. 1990). A retrospective survey of 612 HIV-related admissions in Scotland indicated that there was no excess of female admissions except for detoxification, investigation of episodes of loss of consciousness and urinary tract infections (Willocks et al. 1991). The other problem faced by women, however, is cervical dysplasia, and the more severe dysplasia occurs with increasing immunosuppression which seems to be connected with Human Papilloma Virus (Schafer et al. 1990; Vermund et al. 1990).

A Spanish study of 289 patients with AIDS revealed a median survival of just over one year or 385 days (Batalla et al. 1989). They were able to identify a number of factors influencing survival which included: age, median survival 135 days for those over 45 years but 625 days for those under 45; gender, 436 days for women and 366 days for men; risk group, 744 days for drug users and 253 days for male homosexuals; year of diagnosis, 72 days for those diagnosed before 1986 and 512 days for those diagnosed in 1986 or later years; and index diagnosis, 625 for extrapulmonary tuberculosis but 339 days for other opportunistic infections.

There has been a marked improvement in the survival of patients with AIDS, particularly of those with PCP (Harris 1990; Lemp et al. 1990); the estimated one-year survival increased from forty-three per cent for those diagnosed in 1984–5 to 54.5 per cent for those diagnosed in 1986–7. The gain in survival was observed in homosexual men and in intravenous drug users of both sexes, in all age and racial groups in the USA. Better diagnosis and treatment, particularly the introduction of zidovudine in 1986, may have contributed to the decline in mortality.

MANAGEMENT

Before the advent of HIV infection, drug use itself had a relatively low mortality, with alternating periods of abstinence and drug use followed by natural recovery (Ritson and Plant 1977; Robertson and Bucknall 1986; Waldorf and Biernachie 1979; Wille 1983). The rapid increase in both AIDS-related and non-AIDS narcotic related deaths is such that for every AIDS-related death in a drug user, there is one other as a consequence of such conditions as tuberculosis, endocarditis and bacterial pneumonia. This is the driving force behind harm-reduction, and is the reason why we can no longer rely on spontaneous recovery for drug users (Galli et al. 1988; Stoneburner et al. 1989; Strang and Stimson 1990; Weber et al. 1990). The author's experience is that the average yearly mortality has increased from one to two per cent even during the early years of the epidemic.

The measures to prevent spread of HIV and to reduce possible progression to AIDS are much the same, and it is better therefore when dealing with a patient to concentrate on the advantages to the individual rather than those for society. Management strategies are, however, not absolute. For instance, abstinence from opiates is promoted for a number of reasons but particularly because these drugs reduce resistance to bacterial infections and promote growth of HIV in lymphocytes. However, since there are also data to suggest that continued intravenous drug use accelerates progression to AIDS, measures to reduce drug injection such as the prescription of oral opiate substitute drugs are also important. For those unable or unwilling to give up drug injection, the use of sterile injecting equipment is important because of the otherwise increased susceptibility to further bacterial and viral infections. Many drug users assume that there is nothing to lose from further injecting, but the acquisition of for instance chronic viral hepatitis or endocarditis may significantly shorten their survival (Brettle 1991).

Oral opiate substitute programmes are effective in reducing high-risk injecting behaviour as well as reducing the risk of acquisition of HIV and AIDS (Brettle 1991). Drug users are able to change their high-risk injecting behaviour if given both information and equipment. Outreach intervention programmes have been developed most extensively in the USA to teach the cleaning of injection equipment, and have concentrated on commonly available disinfectants such as bleach, alcohol and detergent. Whilst whole blood is protective against disinfection of HIV, dilute household bleach, seventy per cent isopropyl alcohol and dilute detergent remain effective even in the presence of whole blood, and such compounds should be available to the majority of injecting drug users (Brettle 1991).

A major problem for harm-reduction is the concern that it may encourage existing as well as primary or new drug use. There is no evidence for an increase in the total number of injection drug users as a consequence of needle exchange programmes or even of more drug use among existing users. Harm-reduction for injection drug use is not the only solution for intravenous drug-use-related HIV, but it is a useful intermediate goal although, for many, progression beyond safe injection drug use or oral opiate therapy is unlikely. Blanket harm-reduction measures, however applied in the absence of effective counselling and health education, are not effective in achieving behaviour change (Brettle 1991).

Zidovudine, a nucleoside analogue, has been shown to increase survival and lessen the morbidity of patients with AIDS and ARC. The early toxicity studies noted an association between neutropenia and concurrent paracetamol ingestion, and utilised a four-hourly dosage regime, close monitoring for toxicity and a highly motivated patient group. There was, not surprisingly, concern over whether it was possible to treat current drug users with zidovudine. However, the author's experience with zidovudine and current drug users suggests that it is possible, although there are of course problems (Cowan et al. 1989). The author has seen no adverse reactions with benzodiazepines, opiates, cannabis or alcohol, but we have no experience yet with cocaine. Preliminary studies suggest that long-term opiate use doubles the plasma level of zidovudine (Brettle et al. 1989; Schwartz et al. 1990). While excess toxicity has not yet been reported in most studies of drug users, our own experience suggests that reduced doses may be necessary (MacCallum et al. 1989).

Initiating and maintaining contact with drug users is important not only to reduce the spread of HIV but also to improve their physical health. Despite the problems of HIV, the author and his colleagues and other groups have shown that it is possible to reduce morbidity and lengthen survival with good medical care even among drug users.

REFERENCES

Anonymous (1984): Editorial 'Opiates, opioid peptides, and immunity', *Lancet* i, 774–5.

Batalla, J., Gatell, J., Cayla, J.A., Plasencia, A., Jansa, J.M. and Parellada, N. (1989) 'Predictors of the survival of AIDS in Barcelona, Spain', *AIDS* 3, 355–9.

Brettle, R.P., Jones, G.A., Bingham, J., Spacey, B.E.M., Weatherley, B. and Churchus, R. (1989) Abstract WBO3 presented at the 5th International Conference on AIDS, Montreal.

Brettle, R.P., Farrell, M. and Strang, J. (1990) 'Clinical features of HIV infection and AIDS in drug takers' in Strang, J. and Stimson G.V. (eds), *AIDS and Drug Misuse*, London, Tavistock/Routledge, 38–53.

Brettle, R. P. (1991) 'HIV and harm reduction for injecting drug users', *AIDS* 5, 125–36.

Burns, S.M., Collacott, I.A., Hargreaves, F.D. and Inglis, J.M. (1987) 'Incidence of hepatitis B markers in HIV seropositive and seronegative drug misusers in the Edinburgh area', *Communicable Diseases Scotland (Weekly Report)* 87/08, 7–8.

Carpenter, C.C.J., Fisher, A., Desai, M., Durand, L., Indacochea, F. and Mayer, K.M. (1988) 'Clinical Characteristics of AIDS in Women in south-eastern New England', Abstract 7274, 4th International Conference on AIDS 13–16 June, Stockholm, Sweden.

Centers for Disease Control (1983) 'Classification system for HTLV-III/LAV infections', *Annals International Medicine*, 105, 234–7.

Centers for Disease Control (1987a) 'Revision of the CDC surveillance case definition for Acquired Immunodeficiency Syndrome', *Morbidity and Mortality Weekly Report* 36, no. 1S.

Centres for Disease Control (1987b) 'Tuberculosis and the acquired immunodeficiency syndrome', New York, *MMWR*, 36, 48, 785–90, 795.

Centers for Disease Control (1988) Editorial. 'Increase in pneumonia mortality among young adults and the HIV epidemic – New York /City, United States', *Morbidity and Mortality Weekly Report* 37/(38), 593–6.

Cowan, F.M., Jones, G., Bingham, J., Flegg, P.J., MacCallum, L.R., Whitelaw, J., Hargreave, D., Gray, J.A., Welsby, P.D. and Brettle, R.P. (1989) 'Use of zidovudine for drug misusers infected with HIV', *Journal of Infection* 18, supplement 1, 59–66.

Crovari, P., Penco, G., Valente, A. et al. (1988) 'HIV infection in two cohorts of drug addicts prospectively studied. Association of serological markers with clinical progression', Abstract 4527. *4th International Conference on AIDS*, 13–16 June, Stockolm, Sweden.

Danila, R., Jones, D., Reier, D., Thomas, J., Osterholm, M. and MacDonald, K. (1990) 'A comparison of statewide Minnesota HIV/AIDS surveillance data with a population-based HIV seroprevalence study of child-bearing women in Minnesota', Abstract FC 569. *6th International Conference on AIDS*, San Francisco, USA.

Des Jarlais, D.C., Friedman, S.R., Marmor, M. et al. (1987) 'Development of AIDS, HIV seroconversion, and Potential Co-factors for T4 cell loss in a cohort of intravenous drug users', *AIDS* 1987, 1, 105–11.

Eyster, M.E, Gail, M.H., Ballard, J.O., Al-Mondhiry, N. and Goedert, J.J. (1987) 'Natural history of human immunodeficiency virus infection in haemophiliacs: effects of T-cell subsets, platelet counts and age', *Annual International Medicine* 107, 1–6.

Fauci, A. (1987) 'Immunopathogenesis of HIV', *3rd International Conference on AIDS*, Washington DC. June 1–5.

Flegg, P.J., Jones, M.E., MacCallum, L.R., Bird, A.G., Whitelaw, J.M. and Brettle, R.P. (1989) 'Continued injecting drug use as a cofactor for progression of HIV'. Abstract M.A.P. 92. *5th International Conference on AIDS*, 4–9 June, Montreal, Canada.

Galli, M., Carito, M., Craccu, V. et al. (1988) 'Cause of death in drug abusers – a retrospective survey on 4883 subjects', *4th international Conference on AIDS*, Abstract 4520, 13–16 June, Stockholm, Sweden.

Gatell, J.M., Podzamczer, D., Clotet, B., Ocana, I., Estamy, C., Miro, J.M. and Barcelona AIDS Study Group (1989) 'Incidence of AIDS in Spanish HIV-infected patients', Abstract W.A.P. 55, *5th International Conference on AIDS*, 5–9 June, Montreal, Canada.

Gilks, G.F., Brindle, R.J., Otienok, L.S., Simani, P.M., Newham, R.S., Bhatt, S.M., Lule, G.N., Okelo, G.B.A., Watkins, W.M., Waiyaki, P.G., Were, J.B.O. and Warrell, D.A. (1990) 'Life-threatening bacteraemia in HIV-1 seropositive adults admitted to hospital in Nairobi, Kenya', *Lancet* 336, 545–9.

Goedert, J.J., Biggar, R.J., Weiss, S.H. et al. (1986) 'Three years incidence of AIDS in five cohorts of HTLV-III infected risk group members', *Science* 231, 992–5.

Gold, J., Morlet, A., Nicolas, T., Guinan, J.J. and Stevens, M. (1988) 'Elevation of serum Beta-2 microglobulin associated with decreased CD4 lymphocyte count in HIV infection', *4th International Conference on AIDS*, June 12–16, 1988. Stockholm, Sweden.

Hahn, B.H., Shaw, G.M., Taylor, M.E., et al. (1986) 'Genetic variation in HTLV-III/LAV over time in patients with AIDS or at risk for AIDS', *Science* 232, 1548–53.

Handwerger, S., Mildvan, D., Senie, R. and McKinley, F.W. (1987) 'Tuberculosis and the acquired immunodeficiency syndrome at a New York City Hospital', *Chest* 91, 176–80.

Harris, J.E. (1990) 'Improved short-term survival of AIDS patients initially diagnosed with Pneumocystis carinii pneumonia. 1984 through 1987', *Journal of the American Medical Association* 263, 397–401.

Jaffe, H.S., Abrams, D.I., Anmann, A.J., Lewis, B.J. and Golden, J.A. (1983) 'Complications of co-trimoxazole in treatment of AIDS-associated Pneumocystis carinii pneumonia in homosexual men', *Lancet* 2, 1109–11.

Kaplan, J.E., Spira, T.J., Fishbein, D.B., Pinsky, P.F. and Schoenberger, L.B. (1987) 'Lymphadenopathy syndrome in homosexual men; evidence for continuing risk of developing the acquired immune deficiency syndrome', *Journal of the American Medical Association* 257, 335–7.

Kaslow, A.R., Blackwelder, W.C., Quostrow, D.G. et al. (1989) 'No accelerating immunodeficiency in HIV-1 seropositive individuals. *Journal of the American Medical Association* 261, 3424–9.

Kloser, P., Grigoriu, A. and Kapila, R. (1988) 'Women with AIDS: a continuing study 1987', Abstract 4065 *4th International Conference on AIDS*, 13–16 June, Stockholm, Sweden.

Lacey, C.J.N., Forbes, M.A., Waugh, M.A., Cooper, E.H.,Cooper, J. and Hambling, M.H. (1988) 'Serum b2-microglobulin and HIV infection', Unnumbered sheet. *4th International Conference on AIDS*, 12–16 June, Stockholm, Sweden.

Lambin, P., Lefrere, J.J., Doinel, C., Fine, J.M. and Salmon, C., (1988) 'Neopterin and beta-2 microglobulin in sera of HIV seropositive subjects during a two-year follow-up', *4th International Conference on AIDS*, 12–16 June, Stockholm, Sweden.

Lemp, G.F., Payne, S.F., Neal, D., Temelso, T. and Rutherford, G.W. (1990) 'Survival trends for patients with AIDS', *Journal of the American Medical Association* 262, 402.

Lifson, A.R., Hessol, N., Rutherford, G., O'Malley, P., Barnhart, L., Buchbinder, S., Cannon, L., Bodecker, T., Holmberg, S., Harrison, J. and Doli, L. (1990) 'Natural history of HIV infection in a cohort of homosexual and bisexual men: clinical and immunological outcome', Abstract ThC 33, *6th International Conference on AIDS,* San Francisco, USA.

MacCallum, L.R., Flegg, P.J., Willocks, L.J., Jones, M.E., Cowan, F.M. and Brettle, R.P. (1990) 'Assessment of zidovudine therapy and concurrent opiates use', Abstract SB440, *6th International Conference on AIDS,* San Francisco, USA.

Marthur-Wagh, U., Mildvan, D. and Senie, R.T. (1985) 'Follow-up at 4.5 years on homosexual men with generalised lymphadenopathy'. *New England Journal of Medicine* 313, 1542–5.

Melbye, M., Biggar, R.J., Ebbesen, P. et al. (1986) 'Long-term seropositivity for human T-lymphotorpic virus type III in homosexual men without the acquired immune deficiency syndrome: development of immunologic and clinical abnormalities', *Annals of Internal Medicine* 104, 497–500.

Morris, L., Distenfeld, A., Amorosi, E. and Karpatkin, S. (1982) 'Autoimmune thrombocytopenic purpura in homosexual men', *Annals Internal Medicine* 96, 714–7.

Moss, A.R. and Bacchetti, P. (1989) 'Natural history of HIV infection', *AIDS* 3, 55–61.

Polk, B.F., Fox, R., Brookmeyer, R. et al. (1987) 'Predictors of the Acquired Immunodeficiency Syndrome developing in a cohort of seropositive homosexual men', *New England Journal of Medicine* 316, 61–6.

Polsky, B., Gold, J.W., Whimbey, E. et al. (1986) 'Bacterial pneumonia in patients with the acquired immunodeficiency syndrome', *Annals of Internal Medicine* 104(1), 38–41.

Ratnoff, O.D., Menitove, J.E., Aster, R.H. and Lederman, M.M. (1983) 'Coincident classic hemophilia and 'idiopathic' thrombocytopenic purpura in patients under treatment with concentrates of antihemophilic factor (factor VIII)', *New England Journal of Medicine* 308, 439–42.

Rezza, G., Lazzarin, A., Angarano, G. et al. (1989) 'The natural history of HIV infection in intravenous drug users: risk of disease progression in a cohort of seroconverters', *AIDS* 3, 87–90.

Ritson, E.B. and Plant, M.A. (1977) *Drugs and Young People in Scotland*, Scottish Health Education Unit. Edinburgh.

Rivin, B., Monroe, J., Hubschuman, B. and Thomas, P. (1984) 'AIDS outcome: a first follow-up', *New England Journal of Medicine* 311, 857.

Robertson J.R. and Bucknall, A.B. (1986) 'Heroin users in a Scottish city' *Edinburgh Drug Addiction Study*, West Granton Medical Group, 1 Muirhouse Avenue, Edinburgh EH4 4PL.

Robertson, R.J., Skidmore, C.A., Roberts, J.J.K. and Elton, R.A. (1990) 'Progression to AIDS in intravenous drug users, co-factors and survival', Abstract Th C 649, *6th International Conference on AIDS*, San Francisco, June 1990.

Rothenberg, R., Welfel, M., Stoneburner, R., Milberg, J., Parker, R. and Truman, B. (1987) 'Survival with the acquired immunodeficiency syndrome', *New England Journal of Medicine* 317(21), 1297–302.

Suggeri, P., Sathe, S.S. and Kapila, R. (1988) 'Changing Patterns of Infectious Endocarditis (IE) in parenteral drug abusers (PDA) with Human Immunodeficiency Virus (HIV) Infections', Abstract 8028, *4th International Conference on AIDS*, 13–16 June, Stockholm, Sweden.

Rutherford, G.W., Lifson, A.R., Hessol, N.A. et al. (1990) 'Course of HIV-1 infection in a cohort of homosexual and bisexual men: an 11-year follow-up study', *British Medical Journal* 301, 1183–8.

Savona, S., Nardi, M., Lennette, E.T. and Karpatkin, S. (1985) 'Thrombocytopenic purpura in narcotic addicts', *Annals of International Medicine* 102, 737–41.

Schafer, A., Friedmann, W., Miekle, M., Schwartlander, B. and Koch, M.A. (1990) 'Increased frequency of cervical dysplasia/neoplasia in HIV-infected women is related to the extent of immunosuppression', Abstract SB 519, *6th International Conference on AIDS*, San Francisco, USA.

Schwartz, E.L., Brechbule, A.B., Kahl, P., Miller, M.H., Selwyn, P.A. and Friedland, G.H., (1990) 'Altered pharmacokinetics of zidovudine in former intravenous drug-using patients receiving methadone', Abstract SB432, *6th International Conference on AIDS*, San Francisco, USA.

Selik, R.M., Starcher, E.T. and Curran, J.W. (1987) 'Opportunistic diseases reported in AIDS patients: frequencies, associations and trends', *AIDS* 1, 175–82.

Selwyn, P.A., Schoenbaum, E.E., Hartel, D. et al. (1988a) 'AIDS and HIV-related mortality in intravenous drug users (IVDUs)', Abstract 4526, *4th International Conference on AIDS*, 13–16 June, Stockholm, Sweden.

Selwyn, P.A., Feingold, A.R., Hartel, D., Schoenbaum, E.E. et al. (1988b) 'Increased risk of bacterial pneumonia in HIV-infected intravenous drug users without AIDS', *AIDS* 2, 257–72.

Selwyn, P.A., Hartel, D., Lewis, V.A. et al. (1989) 'A prospective study of the risk of tuberculosis among intravenous drug users with human immunodeficiency virus infection', *New England Journal of Medicine* 320, 545–50.

Selwyn, P.A., Hartel, D., Schoenbaum, E.E., Klein, R.S. and Friedland, G.H. (1990) 'Clinical progression of HIV-related diseases in intravenous drug users (IVDUs) in a prospective cohort study: 1985–1989', Abstract Th C 649, *5th International Conference on AIDS,* June 1990, San Francisco, USA.

Selwyn, P.A., Hartel, D., Schoenbaum, E.E., Davenny, K., Budner, N., Klein, R.S. and Friedman, G.H. (1990) 'Rates and predictors of progression to HIV disease and AIDS in a cohort of intravenous drug users (IVDUs), 1985–1990', Abstract FC III, *6th International Conference on AIDS,* June 1990, San Francisco, USA.

Simberkoff, M.S., El-Aadr. W., Schiffman, G., Rahal, J.J. Jr (1984) 'Streptococcus pneumoniæ infections and bacteremia in patients with acquired immune deficiency syndrome, with report of a pneumococcal vaccine failure', *American Review of Respiratory Disease* 130(6), 1174–6.

Slim, J., Boghossian, J., Perez, G. and Johnson, E. (1988) 'Comparative analysis of bacterial endocarditis in HIV (+) and HIV (-) intravenous drug users', Abstract 8027, *6th International Conference on AIDS,* 13–16 June, Stockholm, Sweden.

Stoneburner, R.L., Des Jarlais, D.C., Benezra, D. et al. (1989) 'A larger spectrum of severe HIV-1 related disease in intravenous drug users in New York City', *Science* 242, 916–8.

Strang, J. and Stimson, G.V. (1990) 'The impacts of HIV: Forcing the process of Change' in Strang, J. and Stimson, G.V., Aids and Drug Misuse, London, Tavistock/Routledge, 4.

Sunderam, G., McDonald, J., Maniatis, T., Oleske, J., Kapila, R. and Reichman, L.B. (1986) 'Tuberculosis as a manifestation of the acquired immune deficiency syndrome (AIDS)', *Journal of the American Medical Association* 256, 362–6.

Taylor, J.G.M., Schwartz, K. and Detels, R. (1986) 'The time from infection with human immunodeficiency virus (HIV) to the onset of AIDS', *Journal of Infectious Diseases* 154, 694–7.

Tubaro, E., Borelli, G., Croce, C., Cavallo, G. and Santiangeli, C. (1983) 'Effect of morphine on resistance to infection', *Journal of Infectious Diseases* 148, 656–6.

Vaccher, E., Saracchini, S., Errante, D. et al. (1988) 'Progression of HIV disease among intravenous drug abusers (IVDA): A three-year prospective study', Abstract 4529, *4th International Conference on AIDS*, 13–16 June, Stockholm, Sweden.

Vermund, S.H., Kelley, K.F., Burk, R.D., Feingold, A.R., Shreiber, K., Munk, G., Schrager, L.K. and Klein, R.S. (1990) 'Risk of human papillomavirus (HPV) and cervical squamous intraepithelial lesions (SIL) highest among women with advanced HIV disease', Abstract SB 517, *6th International Conference on AIDS,* San Francisco, USA.

Verdegam, T.D., Sattler, F.R. and Boylen, C.T. (1988) 'Increased fatality from Pneumocystis carinii pneumonia (PCP) in women with AIDS', Abstract 7271, *4th International Conference on AIDS,* 13–16 June, Stockholm, Sweden.

Vento, S., Di Perri, G., Luzzati, R. et al. (1989) 'Clinical reactivation of hepatitis in anti-HBs-positive patients with AIDS', *Lancet* 1, 332–3.

Waldorf, D. and Biernachie, P.J. (1979) 'Natural recovery from heroin addiction: a review of the incidence literature', *Journal of Drug Issues* 9, 281–9.

Weber, R., Battegay, M., Sollinger, V. and Luthy, R. (1990) 'Non-HIV-associated mortality exceeds HIV-related mortality of HIV-infected intravenous drug users: is there an approach to this challenge in an AIDS outpatient clinic?' Abstract 103, *2nd European Conference on Clinical Aspects of* HIV infection, Brussels.

Weber, R., Ledergerber, B., Opravil, M., Siegenthaler, W. and Luthy, R. (1990) 'Progression of HIV infection in misusers of injected drugs who stop injecting or follow a programme of maintenance treatment with methadone', *British Medical Journal* 301, 1362–5.

Wille, R., (1983) 'Processes of recovery from heroin dependence: relationship to treatment of social change and drug use', *Journal of Drug Issues* 13, 333–42.

Willocks, L., Cowan, F.M., Brettle, R.P., MacCallum, L.R., McHardy, S. and Richardson, A. (1991) 'Early HIV infection in Scottish women', Abstract MB 2433, *7th International Conference on AIDS,* Florence, Italy.

Winkelstein, W. (1988) 'Beta-2 microglobulin level predicts AIDS', *4th International Conference on AIDS,* 12 – 16 June, Stockholm, Sweden.

Young, M.A. and Pierce, P. (1990) 'Natural history of HIV disease in an urban cohort of women', Abstract FB 432, *6th International Conference on AIDS*, San Francisco, USA.

Zulaica, D., Arrizabalaga, J., Iribarren, J.A., Perex-Trallero, E., Rodriguez-Arrondo, F. and Carde, C. (1988) 'Follow-up of 100 HIV-infected intravenous drug abusers', Abstract 4532, *4th International Conference on AIDS*, 12 – 16 June, Stockholm, Sweden.

PART II

PREVENTION AND CONTROLS

8. Does alcohol education work?

GELLISSE BAGNALL

The question posed by the title of this chapter has, at face value, a simple answer – No, alcohol education does not appear to work. Despite its popular appeal as a solution to alcohol misuse, alcohol education has a poor record of proven effectiveness. One review even went so far as to describe past alcohol education as a 'spectacularly wasteful enterprise' (Grant 1986, p. 198). The same author, however, has suggested that there may be more fruitful ways of educating about alcohol. These ideas have been reiterated by Hamburg (1989), who noted the ineffectiveness or even counterproductive nature of much of the drugs education in the USA. At the same time, however, he stressed the need for more research to establish effective ways to 'teach adolescents what they need to know to avoid harmful practices and promote health' (Hamburg 1989, p. 45).

This chapter will pursue these arguments and consider what some of the alternative approaches to alcohol education might be. The discussion will be limited to young people, although not necessarily under-age drinkers. Most of the illustrations will be drawn from research into school or college-based interventions among 'ordinary' young people, that is to say, primary prevention initiatives.

With the exception of those societies where alcohol is totally banned, usually for religious reasons, consumption of 'our favourite drug' (Royal College of Psychiatrists 1986) is widespread. Throughout the world, social and cultural differences have resulted in a range of legislative strategies to control the availability and consumption of alcohol. Any alcohol educational intervention clearly has to operate within the bounds of this more coercive aspect of restrictive practices. This will be assumed for the remainder of the present discussion.

As already implied in the introduction, there is little evidence from the research literature of effective alcohol education (Kinder et al. 1980; Moskowitz 1989; May 1991). Furthermore, as discussed in detail elsewhere (Bagnall 1991a), the methods used to evaluate effectiveness are often lacking in scientific rigour, resulting in questionable conclusions. Despite these difficulties, it is possible to glean some important points from reviews of alcohol education. Most of the positive outcomes appear to be associated with an increase in knowledge about alcohol. It is also clear, however, that this on its own is insufficient to bring about the intended changes in alcohol-related behaviour. Indeed, when information-giving is the principal aim of alcohol or drugs education, there is a proven risk that such interventions may lead to increased substance use (Swisher et al. 1971; Stuart 1974; Kinder et al. 1980; De Haes 1987).

General agreement is evident in the literature concerning some of the major defects which appear to have diminished the effectiveness of school-based substance misuse programmes (Barnes 1984; Weisheit 1983; Goodstadt 1986). These defects include:

- setting of unrealistic programme goals
- absence of a sound theoretical base
- inadequate attention to prevention principles
- limitations in time and scope
- inadequate implementation procedures.

There is no doubt that schools or colleges have an important role to play in educating young people about alcohol and other drugs. Clearly it is unreasonable to expect these educational institutions singlehandedly to counteract a culture which is ambivalent about alcohol and drug use, and which actively promotes such use. However, as argued by Benard et al. (1987) the pivotal role of school in the lives of young people makes it an ideal setting for introducing alcohol education. Trained staff are readily accessible, as are large organised groups of the target population. In addition, the school, as a social institution, already has a 'sense of public legitimacy' (Weisheit 1984, p.473).

In summary, alcohol education generally appears to have been relatively ineffective and has sometimes even been counterproductive. As noted in the next chapter, the same conclusion also applies to drug education. Recommendations for improving this situation include greater attention to theoretical principles, to the need for carefully defined target groups and to the setting of realistic goals for specific alcohol education programmes. As argued elsewhere (Bagnall 1989), there is a need for care, modesty and realism in developing alcohol education initiatives.

WHAT SHOULD ALCOHOL EDUCATION INCLUDE?

As noted above, the focus of this chapter is on education initiatives for young people. Contrary to popular beliefs often reinforced by the tabloid press, most of the available evidence indicates that the majority of young people do not drink excessive quantities of alcohol on a regular basis

(Plant, Peck and Samuel 1985; Marsh, Dobbs and White 1986). In a recent review, May (1992) noted that 'existing data emphasise the *normality* and stability of alcohol use among adolescents and young adults and reflect the pervasiveness of alcohol use across much of the population'. Approximately nine out of ten British adolescents have some experience of alcohol, and there is no doubt that weekend evenings in particular are occasions for older adolescents to drink away from the family home, in pubs and discos. In this context, the major 'misuse' of alcohol is intoxication and its attendant risks of accident and injury. Liver cirrhosis and other physiological problems resulting from long-term excessive consumption are seldom a concern for adolescents. School-or college-based alcohol education ought therefore to focus on the acute rather than the chronic problems of misuse, especially the dangers of inappropriate intoxication.

WHAT THEORETICAL PRINCIPLES SHOULD BE CONSIDERED?

Education to combat the misuse of alcohol can be perceived as education for health. An appropriate theoretical basis for such education would therefore be a theory of health-related behaviour. One such theory which has important implications for alcohol education is the Health Belief Model (Becker 1974). Put simply, this model views the uptake of any health-related behaviour as the outcome of a costs/benefits analysis. Using alcohol-related behaviour as an example, each person will weigh up the advantages and disadvantages for him/herself of, for instance, cutting down the amount of beer consumed during Saturday night drinking sessions.

Related to Becker's Health Belief Model is the Health Action Model proposed by Tones (1989). One of the strengths of this model in relation to alcohol consumption is its identification of the role of feedback. In other words, the Health Action Model takes account of factors which contribute to the maintenance or otherwise of a chosen health-related pattern of behaviour. For example, a decision to reduce the quantity of alcohol drunk on a night out may result in the absence of hangover symptoms, and in parental approval, both of which are likely to be construed as positive feedback. On the other hand, loss of peer-group approval could be construed as negative feedback, thus reducing the likelihood of this behavioural choice being maintained.

In this way, models such as the Health Action Model help to identify some of the influences external to the individual which may facilitate, or act as barriers to, the uptake of healthy behaviour. The importance of this kind of theoretical basis is in its recognition of the situational context and meaning to the individual of particular health-related behaviour, including responsible alcohol consumption. This in turn helps to clarify some of the issues which need to be addressed in developing an alcohol education initiative. But how can such theoretical ideas be translated into practical interventions which aim to encourage the uptake of healthy behaviour?

A CASE STUDY FROM SCOTLAND

This issue was explored as part of a research project conducted between 1986 and 1989 by the Alcohol Research Group at Edinburgh University. A detailed account of this study, including the background and principal findings, has been published as a research monograph (Bagnall 1991b).

The research will be summarised here in order to illustrate two main points:
* • how some of the ideas discussed above were incorporated into the development and evaluation of a school-based intervention to combat alcohol misuse among young people
* • the implications for future alcohol education initiatives.

THE RESEARCH PROJECT

The principal aim of the research was to conduct a controlled prospective study of the effectiveness of a school-based alcohol education programme for students aged twelve and thirteen. The research design had three phases:
* • A pre-intervention survey of alcohol-related knowledge, attitudes and behaviour
* • Development and teaching of a short alcohol education package
* • Post-intervention survey.

Five experienced health/social education teachers were involved in the development of the alcohol education materials. This ensured the relevance of both the content and process of the new package to existing health education curricula. Nine participating schools were selected from three regions of Britain – Highland Region in Scotland, Berkshire in England and Dyfed in Wales. The pre-intervention survey was completed by 1,586 respondents and the post-intervention survey by 1,350 of the original study group.

The alcohol education package was structured to help young people begin to acquire the information and skills necessary to make responsible decisions about alcohol, and to develop knowledge and awareness of the effects of alcohol consumption on themselves and those around them. Given the national statistics on alcohol consumption, a goal of total abstinence would have been unrealistic, and as such would have reduced the credibility of the intervention. Furthermore, alcohol consumption among the target age group is legal in Britain under certain circumstances, thus making it more practical to promote a message of 'low-risk' drinking. This also suggests that while all substance misuse education should be an integral part of a total health education syllabus, there is a need at some stage to make a clear distinction among alcohol, tobacco and illicit drugs.

The education package comprised a manual for teachers and a set of photocopiable worksheets for students. This is now commercially available (Bagnall 1990). Active student participation was encouraged by using a range of analytical and problem-solving activities, including small group discussion and role-playing. Students were guided through a series of open-ended exercises exploring the effects of alcohol consumption on personal and interpersonal behaviour, and the influences affecting how people drink, such as media persuasion, parental attitudes and peer-group pressure. The emphasis on student-centred learning was intended to enable participants to relate the alcohol education to their own personal experience. In this way, the programme arguably satisfied the recommendation (Jessor1982) that account must be taken of the subjective meaning that alcohol use/misuse has for individuals.

In the research project, the package required four hours of classroom time and was successfully implemented by teachers with only a thirty-minute preparatory introduction.

THE OUTCOME – DID THIS INTERVENTION WORK?

The main focus of the research, the evaluation of programme effectiveness, was assessed quantitatively in terms of the shift in alcohol-related knowledge, attitudes and behaviour reported pre- and post-intervention (see Bagnall 1991b). The principal finding was that the young people exposed to the alcohol education showed a significantly greater increase in alcohol-related knowledge than did the controls. Although attitudes towards alcohol appeared to be unaffected by the intervention, a consistent pattern emerged for alcohol-related behaviour. Control group pupils (that is, those who did not receive the alcohol education) were more likely than the intervention group to have increased, between the two surveys,

- the recency of their drinking
- the quantities of beer and wine drunk on the last occasion
- the maximum quantity of alcohol drunk in one session.

It was therefore concluded that the approach to school-based alcohol education adopted in this study had a modest but positive impact on the target population.

IMPLICATIONS AND FUTURE DIRECTIONS
FOR ALCOHOL EDUCATION

The results of this research reinforce those from other evaluation studies, in tobacco education (Gillies 1986; Vartiainen et al. 1986) and in multi-substance education (Hansen et al. 1988). One common thread in these positive outcomes is the 'social influences' approach, that is one which encourages young people actively to address influences on their substance use such as peer-group and other social pressures. This approach would therefore seem a promising direction for the development of future initiatives. In 1982, Grant, in recommending sustained interventions, noted that 'most youth-targeted alcohol education programmes take little account of either parents or peers'. This led him to argue for an approach to such education 'which dealt with the influences (parents, peers, the media) upon young people's drinking'.

Clearly it takes time for new developments to be researched and, more importantly, evaluated. Added to this in the British context is the reality that school-based alcohol education, as part of social/health education, receives low priority in the curriculum. Nevertheless, it could be argued that the ongoing reforms to the curriculum in both the Scottish and English education systems present an ideal opportunity to implement an alcohol education initiative, guided by the recommendations discussed in this chapter.

In England, the Portman Group, a drinks industry initiative to combat alcohol misuse, is currently collaborating with the Health Education Authority to provide a series of regional conferences for alcohol educators. The principal aim of this activity is to pool information and ideas on what practitioners perceive as current best practice in alcohol education. The conclusions of this exercise should provide useful input into the development of future initiatives.

The Advisory Council on Alcohol and Drugs Education (TACADE), a UK charity, received funding in 1990 from the Portman Group to run a series of alcohol education training days for teachers throughout England and Scotland. The intention is that educational staff who attend these courses will go back to their schools and work with colleagues to implement some formal alcohol education.

In the Scottish education system since 1990, students aged between fourteen and sixteen have had the opportunity to follow a series of short 'Health Studies' courses. Some of these include alcohol education, for example in a module entitled *Healthy Risks*. The issues raised in these courses are introduced in increasing depth at several stages, and include healthy lifestyles, emotional development and taking responsibility. The interesting innovation in this development is a formal assessment component, in that successful completion of any one of these forty-hour courses is recognised for certification by the national examination body, the Scottish Examination Board.

Also in Scotland, the Health Education Board for Scotland (formerly known as the Scottish Health Education Group), in collaboration with the Scottish Consultative Council on the Curriculum (SCCC), recently distributed to all schools a report which considers the management and delivery of health education for ten- to fourteen-year-olds. This report

(Scottish Health Education Group, 1990a) covers programme planning, curriculum development, home/school relations and staff training implications. To accompany this document for professional practitioners, a pamphlet for parents of ten- to fourteen-year-olds has been delivered to homes throughout Scotland. This publication aims to explain to parents what primary and secondary schools are trying to do in health education 'as a contribution to strengthening the partnership between home and school'. In the same year, the Scottish Health Education Group developed an alcohol education package for fourteen- to eighteen-year-old school pupils and other student audiences. This was an innovatory exercise in that it utilised extracts of professional video material originally produced for a BBC television series about alcohol misuse. Copies of the complete package (Scottish Health Education Group 1990b) have been placed in all secondary schools in Scotland at no cost. The content includes video extracts which are intended to be used as 'triggers' to promote group discussion around the issues involved. Social influences such as peer-group pressure and alcohol advertising play a prominent role. Student participation is emphasised, and each of the eight video extracts is accompanied by a pupil workcard with follow-up activities, and teachers' notes with background information.

Many of the initiatives discussed in the concluding section are very recent, and it will be some time before the impact, if indeed any, becomes apparent. It also has to be noted, regrettably, that few new initiatives include a formal evaluation component. Some recent developments, however, especially the examples from Scotland, indicate that health and alcohol educators are aware of many of the issues concerning effectiveness raised by formal research, and that some of these are being incorporated into new initiatives. It may therefore be possible to end this chapter rather more optimistically than it began by concluding, albeit with caution, that alcohol education can be made to work.

REFERENCES

Bagnall, G.M. (1989) in Anderson, D. (ed.) *Drinking to Your Health* – The Allegations and the Evidence, London, Social Affairs Unit.
Bagnall, G.M. (1990) *Alcohol Education – A Teaching Pack*, London, Hodder and Stoughton.
Bagnall, G.M. (1991a) *Alcohol Education for Adolescents – An Evaluation Study*, PhD thesis, University of Edinburgh.
Bagnall, G. M. (1991b) *Educating Young Drinkers*, London, Tavistock/Routledge.
Barnes, G. (1984) 'Evaluation of alcohol education – or re-assessment using socialisation theory', *Journal of Drug Education* 14, 144.
Becker, M. (ed.) (1974) *The Health Belief Model and Personal Health Behavior*, Thorofare NJ, Charles B. Slack.
Benard, B., Fafoglia, B. and Perone, J. (1987) 'Knowing what to do – and not to do – reinvigorates drug education', in *Curriculum Update, Association for Supervision and Curriculum Development*, VA, USA.

De Haes , W.F.M. (1987) 'Looking for effective drug education programmes: fifteen year exploration of the effects of different drug education programmes', *Health Education Research – Theory and Practice* 2, 433 – 8.

Goodstadt, M. (1986) 'School-based drug education in North America: What is wrong? What can be done?' *Journal of School Health* 56, 78 – 81.

Grant, M. (1982) 'Young people and alcohol problems: educating for individual and social change', *Paper given at 10th International Congress of the International Association for Child and Adolescent Psychiatry and allied professions*, July.

Grant, M. (1986) 'Comparative analysis of the impact of alcohol education in North America and Western Europe' in Babor, T. (ed.) *Alcohol and Culture – Comparative Perspectives from Europe and North America*, New York, New York Academy of Sciences, 198–210.

Hamburg, B. (1989) 'Adolescent health care and disease prevention in the Americas', In Hamburg, D. and Sartorius, N. (eds) *Health and Behaviour*, Cambridge University Press.

Hansen, W.B., Johnson, C.A., Flay, B.R., Graham, J.W. and Sobel, J. (1988) 'Affective and social influences approaches to the prevention of multiple substance abuse among seventh grade students: results from project SMART', *Preventive Medicine* 17, 135–54.

Jessor, R. (1982)'Critical issues in research on adolescent health promotion', in Coates, T., Petersen, A. and Perry, C. (eds) *Promoting Adolescent Health*, New York Academic Press.

Kinder, B.N., Pape, N.E. and Walfish, S. (1980) 'Drug and alcohol education programmes: a review of outcome studies', *International Journal of the Addictions* 15, 1035–54

Marsh, A., Dobbs, J. and White, A. (1986) '*Adolescent Drinking*, London, HMSO.

May, C.R. (1991) 'Research on alcohol education for young people: a critical review of the literature', *Health Education Journal* 50, 195–9.

May, C.R. (1992) 'A burning issue?Adolescent alcohol use in Britain 1970–1991', *Alcohol and Alcoholism* (in press).

Moskowitz, J.M. (1989) 'The primary prevention of alcohol problems: a critical review of the research literature', *Journal of Studies on Alcohol* 50, 54–88.

Plant, M.A., Peck, D.F and Samuel, E. (1985) *Alcohol, Drugs and School Leavers*, London, Tavistock.

Royal College of Psychiatrists (1986) *Alcohol: Our Favourite Drug*, London, Tavistock.

Scottish Health Education Group (1990a) *Promoting Good Health – Proposals for Action in Schools*, Edinburgh, Scottish Health Education Group.

Scottish Health Education Group (1990b) *The Really Useful Guide to Alcohol*, Edinburgh, Scottish Health Education Group.

Stuart, R. (1974) 'Teaching facts about drugs: Pushing or preventing?', *Journal of Educational Psychology* 66, 189–201.

Swisher, J.D., Crawford, J., Goldstein, R. and Yura, M. (1971) 'Drug-education: Pushing or preventing?' *Peabody Journal of Education* 49, 68–75.

Tones, K. (1987) 'Role of the health action model in preventing drug abuse', *Health Education Research – Theory and Practice* 2, 305–16.

Vartiainen, E., Pallonen, U., McAlister, A., Koskela, K. and Puska, P. (1986) 'Four-year follow-up results of the smoking prevention program in the North Karelia Youth Project', *Preventive Medicine* 15, 692–8.

Weisheit, R. (1983) 'The social context of alcohol and drug education: implications for program evaluations', in *Journal of Alcohol and Drug Education* 29, 72.

Weisheit, R. (1984) 'Alcohol and drug abuse prevention – implications for delinquency prevention', *Journal of Drug Issues* 3, 473–4.

9. Does drug education work?

JOHN B. DAVIES AND NIALL COGGANS

Drug education is not a single entity. It comes in a variety of shapes and forms, and may be underlain by a number of different philosophies. It may be best to start, therefore, by outlining some of the major divisions; and perhaps the greatest of these is the division between the kinds of approaches to drug education which find popular support among the general public, politicians and other non-specialists, and those favoured by education specialists. This chapter also takes the view that the word 'works' implies for most people a reduction in use, rather than an increase in use, or a move towards safer drug-use practices.

POPULAR VIEWS

Many people feel intuitively that the best way forward on this difficult issue is to try to make people, particularly teenagers, afraid of using or misusing drugs. The 'fear arousal' approach thus employs messages which aim to produce fear in the recipients, the assumption being that this will then serve to deter individuals from using drugs.

The second widespread belief is that people take drugs because they do not have access to accurate information about such substances. The assumption is that if people were provided with such information then they would necessarily decide against drug use.

Third, there is the 'decision implementation' approach, centering on the notion that young people try drugs only because they are pressured into it by a peer group with coercive powers beyond their capacity to withstand. The answer to this problem is to teach young people to refuse the drugs that are offered. 'Say "No" to drugs' campaigns are examples of this approach.

It is worthwhile looking a little more closely at the advantages and limitations of these approaches. This topic has been reviewed in relation to alcohol education in the previous chapter.

FEAR AROUSAL

The great advantage of the fear-arousal approach, where drugs are concerned, is that it makes a great public impact and demonstrates to the world that the scourge of illicit drug use is being tackled in no uncertain terms. In national and international terms, the broadcast intention to stamp out drug misuse crystallises for many people the moral battle between right-thinking individuals and those who would subvert society for their own ends; and the fear-arousing communication fits perfectly into this approach. It is a powerful and compelling message; but unfortunately those are its only virtues.

Research evidence from many sources (Kinder et al. 1980; de Haes and Schuurman 1975; Schaps et al. 1981; Bagnall 1991) reveals that fear arousal does not work with respect to illicit drugs, if 'work' is interpreted as reducing the numbers of people who use illicit drugs, or the frequency of their use by those who do. Furthermore, fear arousal has been known to be an ineffective vehicle for a variety of behaviour-change messages (e.g. sensible drinking; smoking; teeth-brushing) for at least two decades. The fact that it is still a favoured method therefore attests to its value as a piece of rhetoric rather than its efficacy in inducing behaviour change. People seem to like the message, and maybe it helps to win elections. On the other hand, if one takes the politically naive view and suggests that the function of such campaigns is to reduce the incidence and prevalence of illicit drug use, it is possible to point to substantial evidence to the contrary. In a number of outcome studies, most such appeals have been found to achieve nothing. Moreover, use of fear arousal runs counter to the advice of the British Government's Advisory Council on the Misuse of Drugs (1984), and serves to perpetuate negative stereotyping of drug users.

INFORMATION-BASED APPROACHES

The basic premise behind this approach is that people who do dangerous or risky things do so because they lack adequate information about the behaviour in question. Consequently, once such information is provided, the desire to carry out the behaviour will be removed. It is the assumption, presumably, that no rational person would knowingly wish to take risks.

Once again, however, the surface logic of this argument is flawed. People do all kinds of activities involving risk, including climbing mountains, riding motorbikes and taking drugs, for pleasure and excitement and in full knowledge of the dangers involved. The idea that people only want to do 'safe' things is quite simply wrong. Furthermore, it is apparent that in some drug education programmes the approach is disingenuous; opinions sometimes masquerade as 'fact'. An unbiased account has to take on board the fact that the occasional or controlled use of pro-scribed substances is not as dangerous as many people appear to think. Deaths due to illicit drug use in the United Kingdom, for example, are in the region of 300 – 400 per annum: small numbers when compared to the deaths associated with cigarettes, alcohol, road traffic accidents and heart disease, which all number in the tens of thousands. It goes without saying that where a health message stresses 'facts' that conflict with the personal experiences of the recipients, the credibility of the message is seriously undermined. Finally, in evaluation research, the information-based approach, like the fear-arousal approach, has generally yielded little or nothing in terms of reducing illicit drug use, and in some circumstances has actually resulted in *increased* use.

DECISION IMPLEMENTATION

The 'Say "No"' approach has featured in a number of anti-drug pro-grammes, and has been highlighted in the media. It is based on the assumption that most young drug-experimenters are drawn into the habit against their will by powerful peer-group members and lack the assertiveness to decline an offer they do not really want to accept. While this may be true in certain cases, a generalised picture of teenage drug use as arising from the inability of naive innocents to withstand the pressures exerted by others does not conform to available evidence. People take drugs on purpose because they want to; and most young people who take drugs are attracted by the prospect of new and pleas-urable experiences, and a natural desire to find out 'what it is like'. (e.g. Davies and Coggans 1991). Within such a context, teaching people to say 'no' has limited applicability, since it assumes that most of the target population *want* to say 'no' but are unable to do so. This is out of touch with the reality of the situation. The absurdity of the approach can be illustrated with reference to the application of the same strategy to an adult population and an activity which is widespread. Does anyone seriously believe that a campaign teaching people to 'Just say No to driving cars', or 'Just Say No to ski-holidays' would have any impact on sales of cars or ski-holidays? The only people likely to use the strategy are those who already dislike such things.

PROBLEMS WITH THE ABOVE APPROACHES

There are clear reasons for rejecting campaigns based on the above principles as being ineffective at best, and counterproductive at worst. But why do people believe that such approaches work? The problem here is one of evaluation: how does one decide on the effectiveness of a campaign? One very *bad* way of doing this is to ask the recipients if they *think* it works. Using such methods, it is usually possible to show that most people believe that the programme was 'a good idea' and that it has 'worked' in some way. Recently, schoolteachers in a Scottish study reported that they thought drug education in schools had changed attitudes towards drugs, had made children less likely to take them and had a number of other good features. Alas, data from the children who received this education showed no such changes. It is quite easy to obtain verbal reports attesting to the 'success' of a campaign; but such data are not objective measures of outcome success.

THE SCOTTISH EVALUATION

The Scottish national evaluation of drug education assessed the effects of school-based drug education on the attitudes, knowledge and behaviour of young people between the ages of thirteen and sixteen. The study involved questionnaires, group discussions and case studies, and sampled nearly 1,200 pupils, 176 teachers and 106 schools. Fuller details of the study are available in Coggans et al. (1991a, b).

While it was found that one in five young people had experimented with drugs at some time, the prevalence of drug use which was regular or suggestive of problematic use was extremely low. This was particularly marked with those drugs which attract most attention, namely heroin, cocaine and ecstasy, the use of which was very rare in this age group. Exposure to drug education, of whatever type, seemed to have very little bearing on patterns of drug use, which were more a function of age, sex and social class. Drug education, in fact, only influenced the amount of information possessed by the young people in the study.

However, when teachers were asked for their views, most of them expressed the opinion that drug education had a beneficial effect on attitudes to and knowledge about drugs. They also believed that young people would be less likely to take drugs after receiving drug education. Only knowledge appeared to be influenced by drug education.

However, in the light of suggestions in the literature that drug education can sometimes actually *increase* drug use, it is worth pointing out that drug education was *not* associated with *increased* drug use in this particular study.

ASPECTS OF GOOD DRUG EDUCATION PRACTICE

The evaluation nonetheless showed that there were important differences between the ways in which individual teachers and particular schools tackled health education. A number of case studies formed the basis for the conclusions that effective teachers involved in drug (and AIDS) education need to be credible sources of information and to adopt a style of interaction which is neither opinionated nor implicitly moralistic. Similarly, they should be aware that the widely held view that young drug users are somehow personally or socially deficient is inadequate as an explanation. The inadequacy theory of drug use is stereotyping in disguise and often has the appearance of being a code phrase for moral inferiority.

A key concept in drug education is 'decision-making'; that is, enabling young people to make appropriate decisions. In reality, however, decision-making sessions are decision-implementation sessions, with the decision to say 'no' suggested by the teacher. Even in certain drug education packages emphasising the life skills approach, there were cases in which the message simply to say no to drugs was implicit or explicit in the package content. Telling young people what to do is simply unsound practice. Moreover, this sort of drug education has nothing to offer young people already experimenting with drugs.

THE WAY FORWARD
Life Skills

Generally, the way in which drug education is carried out has been subject to change from traditional methods, outlined at the beginning of this chapter, towards pupil-centred learning, interactive educational processes and cross-curricular permeation. The 'life skills' approach (Botvin et al. 1984, 1990; Hopson and Scally 1980; Jessor and Jessor 1977) has been adopted widely in standard drug education packs. These methods include cognitive, affective and behavioural components that aim positively to influence self-esteem, self-assertion, decision-making and communication skills. The life skills approach is a considerable advance on previous methods, to the extent that it sticks to the principles of enabling young people to make decisions for themselves based on accurate information about drugs and their related risks. Nonetheless, without careful handling, 'decision-making' sessions essential in the empowerment of young people and the development of positive health behaviour can degenerate into decision-implementation sessions, with the decision being supplied by the teacher. The effectiveness of these sessions can be severely impaired if young people perceive such directive approaches as opinion.

Harm-reduction

Given the increasing prevalence of drug use among young people, it is argued in many circles that there is a role for drug education which enables young people who will take drugs to minimise any risks associated with the substances which they choose to try or use more frequently.

However, this approach poses a number of difficult questions for drug educators, particularly those who are involved with younger age groups. For example, will this approach encourage drug use among those who might not otherwise have tried drugs? In addition, even when drug educators are personally in favour of this approach, there are clear difficulties in targeting the groups for whom this is most appropriate.

Finally, there is the problem of the acceptability of the approach to parents, school boards and other concerned groups.

On the other hand, those who advocate harm-reduction would argue that catering for the needs of young potential drug users is merely being realistic, and that an approach based on the assumption that education will succeed in eliminating drug use in this age group is out of touch with reality. Moreover, they are following the conclusion of the Advisory Council on the Misuse of Drugs (1984) that both demand-reduction and harm-reduction are valid and necessary for the health of the community.

School as systems

There is a trend towards recognition of the importance of the whole school as a caring and health-promoting system. The role of the school as a caring community and the importance of guidance as a whole school responsibility was extensively discussed in a recent position paper, *More Than Feelings of Concern* (Scottish Central Committee on Guidance 1986). More recently, the Scottish Health Education Group and the Scottish Central Committee on Guidance have produced a wide-ranging set of proposals for the promotion of good health, emphasising the need for a whole-school approach which coordinates policy and permeates health education throughout the curriculum, including various aspects of the 'hidden curriculum' such as teacher/pupil interactions and the codes, standards and values implicit in the way the school operates (Scottish Education Department 1977; Scottish Health Education Group/Scottish Central Committee on Guidance 1990).

The whole-school perspective sees the school as a system in which different aspects of the institution can affect the success of health education. For example, success would be hindered by the lack of a clear policy to which all members of staff are party and by the lack of a management structure designed for the implementation of this policy. School policy in relation to drug (and AIDS) education must reflect the needs of young people to develop attitudes and to make the choices that are both relevant to their present circumstances and the basis for developing healthy lifestyles. There is a need to move towards a harm-reduction perspective in education concerning illegal as well as legal drugs (already evident in alcohol education), to reflect the fact that some people regard trying drugs as being both a rational and a positive choice. It is important to accept the fact that most young people who experiment with drugs, or use drugs occasionally, will probably not encounter serious health consequences.

The development of a dynamic and more realistic approach to drug education demands that these issues be confronted. A broader conception of 'drug education' and a more differentiated view of 'effectiveness' are necessary requirements to the future assessment of drug education.

REFERENCES

Advisory Council on the Misuse of Drugs (1984) *Prevention*, London, HMSO.

Bagnall, G. (1991) *Educating Young Drinkers*, London, Tavistock/Routledge.

Botvin, G.J., Baker, E., Renick, N.L., Filazzola, A.D. and Botvin, E.M. (1984) 'A cognitive-behavioural approach to substance abuse prevention', *Addictive Behaviours* 9, 137–47.

Botvin, G.J., Baker, E., Filazzola, A.D. and Botvin, E.M. (1990) 'A cognitive-behavioural approach to substance abuse prevention: one year follow-up', *Addictive Behaviours* 15, 47–63.

Coggans, N., Shewan, D., Henderson, M. and Davies, J.B. (1991a) 'The impact of school-based drug education', *British Journal of Addiction* 86, 1099–109.

Coggans, N., Shewan, D., Henderson, M. and Davies, J.B. (1991b) *National Evaluation of Drug Education in Scotland*, London, Institute for the Study of Drug Dependence.

Davies, J.B. and Coggan, N. (1991) *The Facts About Adolescent Drug Abuse*, London, Cassell.

De Haes, W. and Schuurman, J. (1975) 'Results of an evaluation study on three drug education models', *International Journal of Health Education* 18, Supplement.

Hopson, B. and Scally, M. (1980) *Lifeskills Teaching*, New York, McGraw-Hill.

Jessor, R. and Jessor, S. (1977) *Problem Behavior and Psychological Development: a Longitudinal Study of Youth*, New York, Academic Press.

Kinder, B.N., Pape, N.E. and Walfish, S. (1980) 'Drug and alcohol education programs: a review of outcome studies, *International Journal of the Addictions* 15, 1035–54.

Schaps, E., Di Bartolo, R., Moskowitz, J.M., Palley, C. and Chugrin, S. (1981) 'A review of 127 drug abuse prevention program evaluations', *Journal of Drug Issues* 11, 17–44.

Scottish Central Committee on Guidance (1986) *More Than Feelings of Concern: Guidance and Scottish Secondary Schools*, Edinburgh, Scottish Consultative Council on the Curriculum.

Scottish Education Department (1977) *The Structure of the Curriculum in the Third and Fourth Years of the Scottish Secondary School* (The Munn Report), London, HMSO.

Scottish Health Eduction Group/Scottish Central Committee on Guidance (1990) *Promoting Good Health: Proposals for Action in Schools*, Scottish Health Education Group, Edinburgh.

10. Advertising and youthful drinking

PHILIP P. AITKEN AND GERARD B. HASTINGS

Most young people in the United Kingdom begin drinking before the age of eighteen (Plant, Peck and Samuel 1985; Marsh, Dobbs and White 1986). There is no single, simple explanation for this. However, it seems reasonable to assume that children will be more likely to drink if encouraged by the behaviour and attitudes of parents and peers. It also seems reasonable to assume that children will be more likely to drink if encouraged by sociocultural pressures beyond the immediate circle of family and friends. Advertising is part of this wider social influence.

THE CONCEPT OF MARKET MATURITY

Spokesmen for the alcohol and advertising industries claim that advertising does not increase consumption in 'mature' markets. In mature markets – static markets or markets which have reached a ceiling – advertising can only redistribute brand shares. Industry spokesmen maintain that the market for alcohol is mature (Waterson 1983).

It is important to note that there are many markets for alcohol. For example, markets vary between countries and between different age, sex and socioeconomic groups within countries. In the present context, it is more realistic to think of a spectrum of markets ranging from immature, dynamic markets of teenagers who are experimenting with alcohol to more mature or static markets of older people in which the proportions of drinkers and amounts consumed are relatively constant. Thus the argument that alcohol advertising affects only brand choice goes against widely held marketing concepts.

ECONOMETRIC STUDIES

Econometric studies attempt to delineate variables – such as advertising, price and income – that predict temporal changes in aggregate alcohol consumption. Industry spokesmen claim that these studies have shown that advertising is not associated with changes in alcohol consumption (Waterson 1983). In fact, the position is more complicated.

First, econometric analyses must be interpreted with caution. Inaccurate measurements and omission of relevant variables can lead to misleading conclusions. It is especially difficult to obtain measures of promotional expenditure. No official advertising statistics are collected, and private surveys cover press and television advertising. Therefore findings may be biased by measurement error. Econometric studies of the consumption of spirits which omit cinema and poster advertising are particularly suspect.

Second, and contrary to industry claims, critical reviews and recent research by Godfrey (for detailed references, see Harrison and Godfrey 1989) suggest that econometric analyses of UK data have shown small positive associations between advertising and alcohol consumption.

Third, and importantly in the present context, econometric studies have little to say about youthful drinking because they have examined the effects of advertising averaged over the whole population. They have not examined relationships between advertising and youthful drinking. It is at least possible that the small association between advertising and alcohol consumption obtained in econometric analyses represents averages of small associations in mature markets of older drinkers and larger associations in immature markets of younger drinkers.

PREVIOUS SURVEYS

The few studies that have used the individual as the unit of analysis suggest that alcohol advertising has a stronger influence on the young (Neuendorf 1987). For example, although Atkin, Hocking and Block (1984) found no relationship between exposure to advertising and alcohol consumption among adults, they did find significant associations between alcohol advertising exposure and beer and liquor consumption among teenagers. This does not indicate the direction of causality; but nevertheless, these associations indicate that alcohol advertising has some kind of reinforcing effect.

Strickland (1983) found a small association between exposure to television alcohol commercials and alcohol consumption among teenagers. It was, however, statistically significant only when other variables were held constant. A crucial problem with this research is that the measure of advertising exposure was based on the amount of time that alcohol was advertised on programmes that respondents claimed to have seen. Thus Strickland assumed that exposure to television programmes necessarily exposes viewers to the accompanying commercials. This may account for the tenuous correlation obtained. In the research by Atkin and his colleagues, measures of *attention* to advertisements were also used to construct the indices of advertising exposure.

RECENT RESEARCH IN SCOTLAND

There were three objectives in research conducted by Strathclyde University's Advertising Research Unit: first, to examine the extent to which alcohol advertisements employ images which are attractive to the young; second, to examine age differences in children's perceptions; third, to see if there are any important differences between under-age drinkers and non-drinkers. If alcohol advertising has a reinforcing or rewarding effect, it would be expected that under-age drinkers would be more aware and appreciative of alcohol advertising.

QUALITATIVE RESEARCH

Industry spokesmen have denied that advertisements for alcohol are aimed at the young (Henry and Waterson 1981). However, there is good evidence that an important part of marketing research involves assessing older teenagers' and young adults' attitudes, which are then considered in developing advertising strategy (Aitken, Leathar and Scott 1988). Given this, it would not be surprising if advertisements aimed at older teenagers and young adults presented qualities which younger teenagers find attractive.

There have been few accounts of the child's view of the imagery used in alcohol advertising. Most accounts have been based on the adult's point of view (Day 1978; Williamson 1978; Jacobson, Atkins and Hacket 1983). For this reason, the author's research began with group discussions with children aged between ten and sixteen years (Aitken, Leathar and Scott 1988; Aitken 1989). Group discussions are ideally suited to examining complex issues such as imagery. Areas are explored and children encouraged to use their own words and select their own priorities.

The children were told that the investigators were interested in their views on the mass media. Thus they were not aware that the researchers were primarily interested in their perceptions of alcohol advertising.

The salience of alcohol advertising was assessed by asking the children which advertisements they had seen recently and which advertisements they liked. Almost all of the advertisements mentioned were television commercials. Most advertisements named by the ten-year-olds were humorous commercials for sweets, soft drinks, breakfast cereals, crisps and toothpaste. However, children of twelve and above, and especially fourteen and above, named alcohol commercials at the beginning of their lists of advertisements seen recently and advertisements that they liked.

All of the groups agreed that they liked humorous commercials. More twelve-year-olds than ten-year-olds mentioned brightness and colour, and some mentioned music and action. The fourteen- and sixteen-year-olds mentioned all of these qualities and additionally emphasised the importance of style. For them, a good commercial would be humorous, bright and colourful, with lively action and style. Children of twelve and above often named alcohol commercials when discussing these qualities.

Later in the discussion, the topic of alcohol advertisements was raised to ascertain the extent to which the children were aware that alcohol advertising is often aimed at particular target groups. The ten-year-olds said that commercials for beers and lagers were aimed at men; the ten year-old girls, but not boys, said that commercials for drinks like Martini were aimed at sophisticated women: 'Ladies ... posh ones' (Girl, aged ten).

The view that commercials are often aimed at specific groups was more prevalent among the twelve-year-olds. Boys and girls in this age group quickly agreed that beer and lager commercials were aimed at men, and commercials for drinks like Martini and Bezique at sophisticated women: 'Tennent's Lager and Skol and all that are all men's drinks, 'cos you never see a woman at a bar ordering a pint of beer' (Boy, aged twelve). 'I think it tries to tell you that if you're going out to dinner with your wife or girlfriend you should give them a drink of Martini!' (Girl, aged twelve).

The fourteen- and sixteen-year-olds' descriptions were more complex. Lager and beer commercials were seen as promoting masculinity, sociability and working-class values: 'They're for the men that go out to pubs and socialise' (Girl, aged fourteen). 'They tend to have the image of the macho-type of man who can get all the girls that he wants' (Boy, aged sixteen). Commercials for drinks like Martini and Bezique were seen as portraying sociability, style, sophistication and attractiveness. They were often seen as being aimed at women: 'That Martini one, she goes about on roller skates, skirt up to here, and a' that' (Boy, aged fourteen). 'Expensive adverts.' 'All sun and sea.' 'Suntanned, bronzed people.' 'You too could look like this if you drink ... ' (Girls, aged sixteen).

Thus, whereas the ten-year-olds' descriptions tended to be tied to what is specifically shown in commercials, the older children increasingly tended to go beyond this and alluded to more complex imagery, in much the same way as adults do.

This is not to say that alcohol commercials are aimed at children. All of the groups agreed that they are aimed at adults. Furthermore, as noted above, there is good reason to believe that alcohol campaigns are often aimed at older teenagers and other young adults. Nevertheless, it is clear that alcohol commercials aimed at older teenagers present imagery which younger teenagers also find attractive.

INDIVIDUAL INTERVIEWS

As mentioned earlier, if alcohol advertising has a rewarding or reinforcing effect on under-age drinking, then we would expect under-age

drinkers to be more aware and appreciative of alcohol advertising
compared with non-drinkers of the same age. These issues were examined in a survey of factors associated with under-age drinking (Aitken
et al. 1988; Aitken 1989).

Individual interviews were conducted with 433 ten-to-seventeen year-
olds in Glasgow. As the vast majority of the advertisements mentioned
in the group discussions were seen on television the survey concentrated
on perceptions of television alcohol commercials. Awareness was measured by asking the children what alcohol commercials they had seen and
by asking them whether they had seen and could identify the brands
shown in nine edited photographs of television alcohol commercials.
Appreciation was measured by asking if they liked any alcohol commercials, whether or not they agreed with statements describing alcohol
commercials (for example, 'they have plenty of action', 'they are boring',
'they are stylish') by like/dislike ratings of photographs of alcohol commercials and by asking them whether or not television advertisements
for alcohol should be banned. Other questions provided measures of
variables associated with under-age drinking (for example, peer-group
drinking, parental attitudes). These were used to assess the extent to
which perceptions of alcohol advertising were associated with under-age
drinking when other predictors were controlled or held constant.

As expected from the group discussions, the majority were very much
aware of television alcohol commercials. For example, although awareness
increased with age, only seven per cent could not name a brand advertised
on television, only six per cent could not identify correctly at least one
photograph of a commercial and sixty-one per cent identified four or more.
A majority named the brands advertised in four lager commercials –
Tennent's, Holsten Pils, McEwan's and Castlemaine XXXX.

More of the younger children said that television alcohol commercials
should be banned: the proportions in favour of a ban decreased from
forty-three per cent at 10 – 11 years to seven per cent at 16 – 17 years.
Despite the younger children's less positive view of this issue, answers
to questions about *specific* commercials indicate that the majority of
children of ten and above enjoy alcohol commercials. For example,
although the proportions increased with age, a majority in each age
group named an alcohol commercial that they liked.

Tennent's and McEwan's Lagers were the most frequently named
favourite commercials. Lager sales have increased considerably over the
past two decades, and much of this growth has been achieved through
appeals to older teenagers and other young adults (Field and Morgan
1985; Buckley 1987). Again, it is clear that alcohol commercials aimed
at older teenagers present qualities that younger teenagers also find
attractive.

Large proportions rated alcohol commercials as having good music (eighty-three per cent), bright colours (seventy-one per cent), plenty of action (fifty-seven per cent) and humour (fifty-one per cent). Only thirty-one per cent said they were boring. Although the older children were more appreciative, there were no significant age differences in ratings of alcohol commercials as being humorous and colourful. However, as predicted from the group discussions, the older children tended to rate alcohol commercials more highly on good music, lively action and style.

There were consistent differences between drinkers and non-drinkers. Drinkers tended to recall more brands advertised and tended to be better at recognising and identifying the brands advertised in the edited photographs of commercials. This indicates that under-age drinkers tend to pay more attention to alcohol commercials. Furthermore, drinkers also tended to be generally more appreciative of alcohol commercials. Proportionally more drinkers than non-drinkers had a favourite alcohol commercial and proportionally more drinkers were against a ban on alcohol commercials. Drinkers also tended to have higher scores on scales measuring alcohol advertising appreciation, liking for humorous alcohol advertisements and liking for alcohol advertisements with modernistic, surrealistic imagery. Thus, in summary, these findings indicate that under-age drinkers are getting more pleasure out of alcohol commercials.

Multiple regression analysis showed that the drinkers' greater awareness and appreciation of alcohol commercials was independent of age, peer-group drinking, perceived parental attitudes towards under-age drinking and a number of other variables. Thus it is unlikely that the associations between perceptions of alcohol commercials and under-age drinking can be explained in terms of uncontrolled associations with other perhaps more important variables.

This does not mean that advertising is more important than other sociocultural influences. Indeed, the weights in the regression equations indicated that increasing age (and all that goes with this in the way of increasing cultural expectations) and peer influences are more important and that parental influences are probably of equal importance.

PRIORITIES FOR RESEARCH

The authors did not examine associations between awareness/appreciation of alcohol commercials and amounts consumed by under-age drinkers. As mentioned above, previous surveys suggest that higher levels of attention to alcohol advertising are associated with higher levels of alcohol consumption among teenagers. However, some of the associations were small and it is likely that other factors, especially peer influences, are more important. Furthermore, these studies did not examine relationships between amounts consumed and *appreciation* of alcohol advertising. Thus there is a need for further research examining alcohol advertising awareness/appreciation and amounts consumed by under-age drinkers.

Finally, the findings described here do not necessarily mean that advertising plays a part in inducing children to *start* drinking. Cause and effect relationships are difficult to disentangle. For example, children may become more aware and more appreciative of alcohol commercials *after* they start drinking. There is a need for prospective studies which are designed to assess to what extent awareness and appreciation of alcohol advertising predict the onset and amount of under-age drinking. Such studies are important because predictors of current drinking behaviour may not necessarily be predictors of future drinking behaviour.

Available evidence has shown that alcohol advertising has a *small* effect on drinking habits (e.g. Plant, Grant and Williams 1983; Grant and Ritson 1983). The evidence presented here does suggest that alcohol advertising reinforces under-age drinking. Studies of youthful drinking should attempt to clarify further the power of advertising to influence alcohol use and misuse.

REFERENCES

Aitken, P.P. (1989) 'Television alcohol commercials and under-age drinking', *International Journal of Advertising* 8, 133–50.
Aitken, P.P., Leathar, D.S. and Scott, A.C. (1988) 'Ten- to sixteen-year-olds' perceptions of advertisements for alcoholic drinks', *Alcohol and Alcoholism* 23, 491–500.
Aitken, P.P., Eadie, D.R., Leathar, D.S., McNeill, R.E.J. and Scott, A.C. (1988) 'Television advertisements for alcoholic drinks *do* reinforce under-age drinking', *British Journal of Addiction* 83, 1399–419.
Atkin, C., Hocking, J. and Block, M. (1984) 'Teenage drinking: does advertising make a difference?' *Journal of Communication* 34, 157–67.
Buckley, S. (1987) 'Why these ads are no joke', *Media Week* 27 November, 19.
Day, B. (1978) *100 Great Advertisements*, London, Times Newspapers, Mirror Group Newspapers, Campaign.
Field, P. and Morgan, A. (1985) 'Hofmeister: a study of advertising and brand imagery in the lager market.' In Channon, C. (ed.) *Advertising Works*, London, Holt, Rinehart and Winston, 70–83.
Grant, M. and Ritson, E.B. (eds) (1983) *Alcohol: The Prevention Debate*, London, Croom Helm.
Harrison, L. and Godfrey, C. (1989) 'Alcohol advertising controls in the 1990s', *International Journal of Advertising* 8, 167–80.
Henry, H.W. and Waterson, M.J. (1981) 'The case for advertising alcohol and tobacco products' In Leathar, D.S., Hastings, G.B. and Davies, J.K. (eds) *Health Education and the Media*, Oxford, Pergamon Press, 115–27.
Jacobson, M., Atkins, R. and Hacket, G. (1983) *The Booze Merchants: The Inebriating of America*, Washington DC, Center for Science in the Public Interest.
Marsh, A., Dobbs, J. and White, A. (1986) *Adolescent Drinking*, London, HMSO.
Neuendorf, K.A. (1987) 'Alcohol advertising: evidence from social science', *Media Information Australia* 43, 15–20.

Plant, M.A., Grant, M. and Williams, A. (eds) (1983) *Economics and Alcohol*, London, Croom Helm.

Plant, M.A., Peck, D.F. and Samuel, E. (1985) *Alcohol, Drugs and School Leavers*, London, Tavistock.

Strickland, D.E. (1983) 'Advertising exposure, alcohol consumption and misuse of alcohol. In Grant, M., Plant, M. and Williams, A. (eds) *Economics and Alcohol*, London, Croom Helm, 201–22.

Waterson, M.J. (1983) *Advertising and Alcohol Abuse*, London, Advertising Association.

Williamson, J. (1978) *Decoding Advertisements*, London, Marion Boyers.

11. Scottish licensing reforms

JOHN C. DUFFY

INTRODUCTION

This chapter deals with regulations for the sale of alcoholic drinks in premises within which drinking takes place, and with changes in these arrangements following the Licensing (Scotland) Act of 1976. Further changes have taken place as a result of the Law Reform (Miscellaneous Provisions) (Scotland) Act of 1990, and these will be described briefly at the end of the chapter.

Alcoholic drinks in Scotland may be sold for consumption on or off the premises where the sale takes place. Establishments which sell alcohol for consumption off the premises only, such as licensed grocers, super-markets and wine merchants' shops, do so under an 'off-sales licence', and, while changes in the arrangements for off-sales in such premises have occurred, these are not the topic of this chapter. It is noted in passing, however, that despite such changes as have taken place, off-sales licences continue to prohibit the retail sale of alcoholic drinks in these establishments on Sundays.

Prior to 1976, there were four main types of certificate available to establishments for the sale of alcoholic drinks for consumption on the premises. The most common form of licence, the public house licence, regulated the sale of alcoholic drinks in premises which might be described as bars pure and simple. This permitted the sale of alcoholic drinks on the premises from the hours of 11 a.m. to 2.30 p.m. and 5 p.m. to 10 p.m. on Monday to Saturday inclusive. Sale of alcoholic drinks in these premises on Sundays was forbidden.

The hotel licence, as its name implied, could be granted only to premises satisfying certain criteria in respect of availability of accom-modation to rent and meals. This licence permitted the sale of alcoholic drinks during the same hours as the public house licence but also allowed

Sunday opening from the hours of 12.30 p.m. to 2.30 p.m. and 6.30 p.m. to 10 p.m. A restaurant licence allowed the sale of alcoholic drinks to customers having a meal. Permitted hours were as under a hotel licence, with an extra hour at the end of each session. Some establishments had both a public house licence and a restaurant licence, which permitted the premises to operate as a bar during the permitted hours for public houses.

The fourth type of licence applied to registered clubs, whose permitted hours were essentially the same as for the hotel licence. All of these licences were granted by decision of the appropriate district licensing court, subject to considerations of suitability of premises, objections by interested parties etc.

In all cases, extensions to the basic permitted hours could be applied for in respect of specific events on specific dates. However, except in unusual circumstances, 'blanket' permission for extension of hours on a range of dates was not available. Extension had to be applied for in respect of each particular date for which it was sought.

THE LICENSING (SCOTLAND) ACT 1976

A total of forty-eight changes to existing policy in this area were recommended by a Government committee set up to review Scottish licensing arrangements (Clayson 1972), and some of these were implemented in the Licensing (Scotland) Act of 1976. The major changes were to permitted hours, which were extended by one hour at the end of the evening session for public houses and hotels from 13 December 1976, while public houses were permitted to apply for a licence for Sunday opening from October 1977. A further change, not thought to be of great significance at the time, was that applications could be considered for regular extensions of permitted hours. These would be available to public houses for Monday to Saturday only, and to hotels and clubs on all days of the week. A refreshment licence was introduced, which permitted the sale of alcoholic drinks in premises without a bar, which served snacks and meals, and in which children could be present although not served with alcoholic drinks. For a full description of Scottish licensing arrangements following the 1976 Act the interested reader is referred to Jameson (1988).

Of these changes, undoubtedly the most controversial were Sunday opening of public houses and the possibility of regular extensions of permitted hours. The extension of permitted hours by one hour at the end of the evening session was seen as a natural response to the particular problem of accelerated drinking by bar patrons towards the 10 p.m. deadline and the consequent public order problem of the streets of cities filling up shortly after 10 p.m. with all the patrons of all the public houses and hotels.

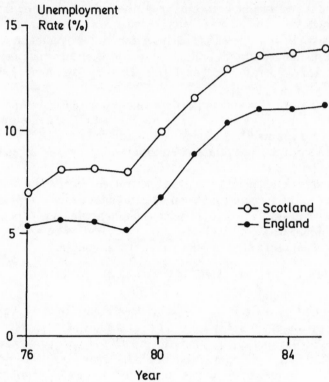

Figure 11.1 Unemployment in Scotland and England (1976–85).
(Central Statistical Office 1976, 1981, 1986, 1987)

The first impact of the possibility of regular extensions was a trend towards afternoon opening of public houses, in what amounted to 11 a.m. to 11 p.m. opening hours. This was most obvious in the major cities of Scotland, where there existed sufficient trade to make such opening profitable. Unfortunately, due to staff policy in the Scottish Office, statistics regarding the number of grants of regular extensions of permitted hours ceased to be collected after 1980, when 5,604 such extensions were granted. At the same time, regular extensions of permitted hours began to be granted to cover other periods on weekdays, to the extent that it is anecdotally reported that one could drink in public houses in Edinburgh at any time of the day or night, with the exception of the period 4 a.m. to 5 a.m., on any day except Sunday.

It is certainly the case that public houses can be found in Scotland which open at 5 a.m., although these are extremely unusual, and their grants of regular extensions to cover such unlikely hours relate to the presence nearby of establishments employing shift-workers. Needless to

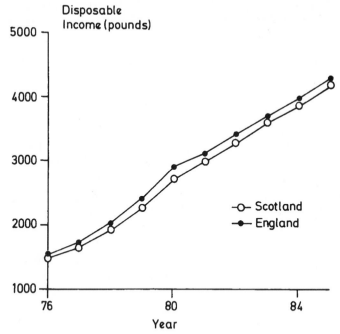

Figure 11.2 Disposable income per capita in Scotland and England
(1976–85). (Central Statistical Office 1976, 1981, 1986, 1987)

say, however, their clientele at these times is not always entirely com-
posed of night workers on their way home. Regular extensions until the
early hours of the morning are often associated with bars providing
entertainment, and it is not difficult to find public houses open after
midnight in central city areas.

ALCOHOL-RELATED HARM

A short-term study (Bruce 1980), conducted about three months before
and after the changes, found that after liberalisation there was no
difference in average alcohol consumption, there was a small decline in
the rate of consumption per person, and the prevalence of accelerated
drinking towards the end of the evening session had significantly reduced. The general conclusion was that there had been no short-term ill
effects and possibly some benefit from the reform. In a further report,
Knight and Wilson (1980) reported on the results of three surveys,
conducted in 1976 (before), 1977 (after the 'extra hour') and 1978 (after
Sunday opening). They investigated a number of aspects of drinking
pattern, leisure activities and public perception and opinion of the
changes, but attention is restricted here to alcohol consumption. Overall,
they found no significant increase in total weekly consumption over the

three periods, but found evidence of an increase in weekly consumption by men aged forty-five or under after Sunday opening, which was offset to some extent by a decrease in consumption by older men. A later report (Office of Population Censuses and Surveys 1985), again based on population survey in Scotland, showed that weekly alcohol consumption by men did not change between 1976 and 1984, although consumption by women rose by about one third over the same period. In common with the other studies described above, it is difficult to interpret these results due to the absence of a control comparison.

Six years after the changes, Clayson (1984) argued that the relaxation of the licensing laws had been of benefit to the Scottish community, despite the uneasy forebodings of those opposed to liberalisation. In a comparison of Scottish statistics in the six years before and after the reforms with similar statistics from England and Wales, where no change in licensing had taken place, he found that while Scottish convictions for drunkenness showed a decline after liberalisation, in England and Wales there was an increase over the same period. Drunk driving convictions showed a 1.2 per cent increase in Scotland after liberalisation, but a thirty-six per cent increase in England and Wales. However, average liver cirrhosis mortality showed a forty-five per cent rise in deaths in Scotland, compared to a seventeen per cent rise south of the border. Convictions for violent crime had increased at a higher rate in England and Wales during the period than in Scotland.

Saunders (1985) criticised Clayson's interpretation of the above findings as indicating a beneficial effect. His most salient criticism related to the increase in liver cirrhosis mortality, which he interpreted as a negative consequence of liberalisation. He made minor, and in some cases misguided criticism of Clayson's other findings. For example, he showed that there was quite a high temporal correlation between the figures for drunkenness convictions in both the north and the south, and seemed to interpret this as vitiating Clayson's finding of a difference. He also mistakenly suggested that Scotland had been particularly adversely affected by the economic recession and increase in unemployment following the election of the first Thatcher government in 1979 (this point arises again later).

Duffy and Plant (1986) examined trends in a number of health and public order indicators over the seven-year periods before and after the change in Scotland using experience in England and Wales as a control comparison. They found that mortality from liver cirrhosis, known to be higher in Scotland, had risen in both areas over the period under consideration, with the ratio of mortality rates (Scotland : England and Wales) showing a slight increase throughout the fourteen year period in both sexes, but with no evidence of any particular influence associated with the events of late 1976. They found a similar pattern in recorded mortality due to alcohol dependence and total alcohol-related mortality.

Psychiatric inpatient admissions for alcoholism/alcohol dependence and alcoholic psychosis showed a clear downward trend over the entire period in the rate ratios in both sexes, with again no striking evidence of a change around 1976, and a similar finding was evident for first admission rates for the same conditions.

Public order offences resulting in convictions for drunkenness were not analysed separately by sex, but the authors found that the ratio of the Scotland to England and Wales rates increased up to 1975 and declined thereafter. It seemed unlikely that the decline in 1976 could be due to a change which took effect in the last month of that year, and as a result it was merely suggested that the continuation of this trend, in which 1976 might simply have been a random fluctuation, could be due in part to liberalisation of licensing laws, although other legal changes, in particular the Criminal Justice (Scotland) Act 1980 could be expected to perpetuate a decline.

Drink-driving conviction rates were stable over the period in Scotland, whereas they increased south of the Border, which led to a steadily decreasing rate ratio, and again no evidence of change related to 1976.

The overall conclusion was that neither extreme benefit nor extreme harm had resulted from the changes, and that the Clayson report was correct in stating that 'Licensing, a negative and restrictive process, can play only a strictly limited part in the control of alcohol misuse'.

In published criticism of this work, Prichard (1986) suggested that the reason why alcohol consumption and related problems had not increased in Scotland relative to England and Wales following liberalisation was that Scotland had been more adversely affected by economic recession, a point made earlier by Saunders (1984). As this question has not yet been addressed adequately in the literature in this context, graphs are reproduced here of percentage unemployment in Scotland and England (Figure 11.1) and of disposable income per capita (Figure 11.2) (Central Statistical Office 1981, 1986, 1987).

It can be seen that there is no evidence of divergent trends after 1976. A further criticism concerned administrative policy as an influence on conviction rates. This undoubtedly valid observation was in fact made in the original paper (Duffy and Plant 1986). It is quite possible that the differential trends in rates of these phenomena in Scotland and in England and Wales are simply the results of differential trends in the administration of the relevant law. The question is virtually incapable of resolution. The latter point was reiterated by Eagles and Besson (1986), who also pointed out that many more patients with alcohol problems were admitted to general hospitals with other diagnoses than were admitted to psychiatric hospitals for alcoholism/alcohol dependence, and that in the north-east of Scotland an increasing trend had been observed in the rates of such admissions. In the absence of a control comparison, the relevance of this remark to the possible effect of licensing liberalisation is elusive.

One final piece of research in this area might be mentioned. In 1987, it was reported that a dramatic increase in the frequency of alcohol taken in association with self-poisoning had been observed in west Fife, following liberalisation of licensing laws (Northridge, McMurray and Lawson 1986). The authors also noted that total admissions for self-poisoning had increased with relaxation of the licensing laws. One deficiency in their approach is that rather than examine trends over the whole period, they compared averages over the periods before and after change, which since there was an increasing trend over the earlier period was bound to lead to the second period having a higher average. The absence of a control comparison in their work was pointed out by Lockhart and Baron (1987), who had observed a similar pattern in overdose rates in west London. Platt (1987) showed that different trends in self-poisoning had been observed in Edinburgh from those reported in Dunfermline, and observed that the increase in self-poisoning in Edinburgh had started in 1972, and hence was unlikely to be associated with changes taking place in late 1976.

DISCUSSION

It is undoubtedly true that the range of evidence considered to date regarding the influence of licensing liberalisation on alcohol-related harm in Scotland is extremely limited. Researchers are essentially restricted to using routinely collected data which are available both for Scotland and England and Wales for periods before the change took place. However, it seems unlikely that major adverse effects, either on public health or public order would pass unnoticed by the agencies dealing with these problems, and in the absence of any reports of such effects it is reasonable to take routine sources as a guide. The conclusion must therefore be, that, for a period of at least seven years following the changes there were no notable beneficial or adverse effects on levels of alcohol-related harm. Further study may detect such, but comparisons with England and Wales will be complicated by the changes which took place in licensing laws in those countries in the late 1980s.

In Scotland, too, the law has changed recently. The Law Reform (Miscellaneous Provisions) (Scotland) Act (1990) made further changes to Scottish licensing arrangements. The Act extends permitted hours on weekdays to cover the afternoon period during which a regular extension of permitted hours had to be applied for, effectively making the permitted hours 11 a.m. to 11 p.m. A further change allows holders of public house licenses to apply for regular extensions of permitted hours on Sundays. The sale of alcoholic drinks in off-licences on Sundays remains prohibited. The effect of these changes will no doubt be the subject of future research and debate.

REFERENCES

Bruce, D. (1980) 'Changes in Scottish drinking habits and behaviour following the extension of permitted evening opening hours', *Statistical News* 48 (unpaginated).

Central Statistical Office (1976) *Regional Statistics* 12, London, HMSO

Central Statistical Office (1981) *Regional Trends* 16, London, HMSO

Central Statistical Office (1986) *Regional Trends* 21, London, HMSO

Central Statistical Office (1987) *Regional Trends* 22, London, HMSO

Clayson, C. (1984) 'Licensing law and health: the Scottish experience' In *Policy Forum: Licensing Law and Health Report*, London: Action on Alcohol Abuse.

Clayson, C. (1972) *Report of the Departmental Committee on Scottish Licensing Law*, Edinburgh, HMSO.

Duffy, J.C. and Plant, M.A. (1986) 'Scotland's liquor licensing changes: an assessment', *British Medical Journal* 292, 36–9.

Eagles, J.M. and Besson, J.A.O. (1986) 'Scotland's liquor licensing changes', *British Medical Journal* 292, p.486.

Jameson J.N.St.C. (1988) *A Practical Guide to Scottish Licensing Law*, Edinburgh, Jameson Publishing.

Knight, I. and Wilson, P. (1980) *Scottish Licensing Laws*, London, HMSO.

Lockhart, S.P. and Baron, J.H. (1987) 'Association between Scottish liquor licensing laws and admissions for self-poisoning', *British Medical Journal* 294, p.116.

Northridge, D.B., McMurray, J. and Lawson, A.A.H. (1986) 'Association between liberalisation of Scotland's liquor licensing laws and admissions for self-poisoning in west Fife', *British Medical Journal* 293, 1466–68.

Office of Population Censuses and Surveys (1985) 'Drinking and attitudes to licensing in Scotland', *OPCS Monitor* 55.

Platt, S.D. (1987) 'Association between Scottish liquor licensing laws and admissions for self-poisoning', *British Medical Journal* 294, 116–17.

Prichard, B. (1986) 'Scotland's liquor licensing changes', *British Medical Journal* 292, p.486.

Saunders, W. (1985) 'Licensing law: the Scottish experience – a reply to Clayson', *AAA Review* July/August 1985, 3–14.

12. Drink and driving

JAMES A. DUNBAR

INTRODUCTION

Based on the irrefutable links between alcohol levels and motor vehicle crashes, drinking and driving laws were passed in many countries during the 1960s. In the Road Traffic Act of 1967, Britain introduced a legal limit of 80mg/100ml in the blood of drivers. This law was enforced by the police breathalysing drivers involved in accidents, committing moving traffic offences, or whose driving was impaired. The initial result produced an eleven per cent reduction in the national crash toll, then appeared to decline, although over a seven-year period at least 5,000 deaths and 200,000 crashes were judged to have been saved as a result.

The diminishing deterrent effect of the law was attributed to many reasons, including the low perceived probability of a driver being breath-tested during his/her trip; estimates placed the likelihood at only one chance in hundreds, if not thousands.

Concern about the decreasing effectiveness of the 1967 legislation led to the establishment of a Government Committee of Inquiry, which reported in 1976.

There was no government action until 1983, when the road traffic law was amended to permit evidential breath-testing and the high-risk offender was recognised as a driver convicted on two occasions within ten years or with an alcohol level of 200mg/100ml of blood, or who refused to give a specimen.

In Britain, there are 100,000 drinking and driving offences, 1,000 deaths and over 20,000 serious injuries each year. The cost to the country is estimated at around £700 million.

Driving under the influence of alcohol has diminished. Public attitudes have hardened immeasurably, but government has continued to lag behind public opinion. Drinking and driving is reported and discussed by the media, being covered in feature articles, editorial comment and on television news and radio programmes. Even soap opera plots refer to it. There is an increasing alliance of interested parties including government, police, motoring organizations, insurers, the churches and the medical profession. This has certainly raised the level of general interest in the drinking and driving issues.

The Department of Transport's regular monitoring indicates that the frequency of alcohol-impaired driving has halved over the last five years and that drinking and driving deaths fell below 1,000 per annum in 1987 for the first time. Over the last ten years, not only has the absolute number of drinking and driving deaths fallen, but the proportion of alcohol-related deaths has also fallen from one third of all accidents to one quarter. Police enforcement levels have increased dramatically. On average, the police forces have increased breath-testing by thirty per cent per annum each year since 1987, though it should be said that there is a wide variation between the most and the least active forces. The Department's own opinion survey has shown that eighty-one per cent of those who admit drinking and driving are in favour of random breath-testing (National Opinion Polls 1989).

Nevertheless, alcohol-impaired driving remains the single most preventable cause of road traffic accidents.

PROGRESS AGAINST DRINKING AND DRIVING
THE CAMPAIGN FOR RANDOM BREATH TESTING

Government has been left in no doubt by all relevant individuals and organizations, the media and opposition political parties, that the single most important counter-measure for drinking and driving is random breath-testing. (Arthurson 1985; Aberg, Engdahl and Nilsson 1986; Dunbar, Penttila and Pikkarainen 1987; Peacock 1992). Only the alcohol industry, including the Brewers' Society, is opposed to it.

It is important that the distinctions between unfettered discretion, *random stopping* and *random breath-testing* be understood. *Random breath testing* means the use of visible, static roadside checkpoints at which all or a genuinely random sample of all drivers passing through are required to give a breath test. At the checkpoint, the police do not need specific grounds to suspect a driver of having consumed alcohol in order to require him or her to give a breath test.

Unfettered discretion would permit the police to operate random breath-testing defined as above, but it would also permit them, outside the context of a roadside checkpoint, to stop any motorist at any time solely for the purpose of requiring a breath test.

The overwhelming weight of scientific evidence points to the effectiveness of an increased frequency of breath-testing as a deterrent to drinking and driving. The only room for dispute that remains concerns the most effective method of conducting breath tests in order to maxi-mise their deterrent value and to increase the perceived probability of detection.

It is sometimes suggested that the fact that the police already possess the power of random stopping or 'targeted testing' makes random breath-testing unnecessary. This argument is invalid. Consolidation of existing police powers to permit the more intensive use of random stopping would reduce the accident toll on our roads, but it would have considerably less effect than random breath-testing. New Zealand has conducted inten-sive random stopping blitzes, but this has been less effective than random breath-testing in neighbouring Australia. The reason for this is not difficult to find. Random stopping or targeted testing is simply an inferior version of random breath-testing. It is more cumbersome to operate, more likely to alienate the public, and also less efficient because it has a lower profile and so less deterrence. Random stopping is more cumbersome because, having stopped the vehicle, the police then have to examine or question the driver in order to ascertain if there is 'due cause' to justify a breath test. This procedure is time-consuming and likely to be irritating to the driver.

It is also less efficient because experience suggests that recognising someone who may have been drinking simply by what is necessarily a cursory inspection of his or her demeanour is in fact rather difficult. In one Swedish experience, the majority of drivers with alcohol levels greater than 50mg/100ml were not suspected by police at a checkpoint of having alcohol in their bodies and were not therefore tested. Nearly half of those in excess of 150mg/100ml were similarly not suspected of having consumed alcohol, and were also allowed through the checkpoint without being tested (Trafiknykterhetsbrott Forslag 1970). Thus, ran-dom stopping is clearly likely to result in a substantial number of drivers being taught precisely the wrong lesson – that they can still drink and drive and avoid detection, even at a police checkpoint. Moreover, a high proportion of these drivers will be problem drinkers who are known to be particularly likely to cause accidents. Problem drinkers, because of their high tolerance, tend to be able to consume even large amounts of alcohol without obviously appearing to be under the influence and, thus, without arousing suspicion.

Intensive use of existing police powers in relation to the breath-test-ing of drivers who have committed moving traffic offences also runs the risk of alienating the public when it results in what they are likely to perceive as an overly enthusiastic attempt by the police to penalise trivial traffic violations simply in order to have a legitimate excuse to demand a breath test.

In Fife, where the police have reached levels of breath-testing compa-rable with random breath-testing campaigns in other countries, the local press has published a number of letters of complaint describing such police tactics as objectionable and stating that in the writers' opinion it would be far better for the police simply to be given the power of random breath-testing. Paradoxically, the more intensive use of existing police powers, including the power of random stopping or targeted testing, is likely to be only partially effective in reducing drinking and driving and, moreover, runs the considerable risk of impairing relations between police and public. In contrast, experience in other countries shows that random breath-testing increased in popularity after its introduction and is most popular in precisely those areas where it is most frequently carried out.

In summary, compared with random stopping, random breath testing is more effective as a deterrent to ordinary social drinkers; it is a more efficient method of catching problem drinkers; and it is easier and less time-consuming to operate, the simple 'blow and go' of random breath-testing only taking a few seconds in contrast to the lengthier and more irksome random stop procedure. Experience in other countries suggests that the police did not need additional resources for random breath-testing and that random breath-testing saves more money than it costs.

Random breath-testing is also superior to unfettered discretion, partly for the reasons given above (the need to maximise deterrence, and police difficulties in knowing which drivers to test) and also because unfettered discretion, without the legal constraints that can be built into the checkpoint system, is potentially open to abuse and likely, therefore, to be opposed on civil libertarian grounds. Random breath-testing avoids the possibility of individuals or groups of drivers being unfairly picked on.

Random breath-testing is thus the most effective method of reducing alcohol-impaired driving. It has been proved successful both in Australia, which has a worse drink-driving record than Britain's, and in Norway and Sweden, which have a better record than Britain's. Based on the Swedish experience, the National Audit Office estimated that random breath-testing would save 500 lives a year in Britain (Department of Transport 1988).

In Finland, random breath-testing has reduced the number of alcohol-impaired drivers on the roads by two thirds, and there is no reason to believe that it would be less successful in Britain.

IMPROVED IDENTIFICATION FOR PROBLEM DRINKING DRIVERS

For a quarter of a century, it has been known that problem drinkers are disproportionately represented among drinking and driving offenders. A conviction is sometimes the early sign of a chronic alcohol problem. In contrast, social drinkers could not reach the blood alcohol levels of most offenders without unpleasant symptoms. These problem drinkers should be identified and required to convince the courts that their driving no longer represents a danger to other road users before their driving licences are restored.

One third of alcohol-impaired drivers over the age of thirty had abnormal gamma glutamyl transferase (GGT) measurements at the time of their arrest (Dunbar et al. 1983). Among drivers who required a driving licence for their work, and older drivers, a disproportionately high number had raised gamma glutamyl transferase activity, indicating problem drinking. In drivers over the age of thirty a strong association was found between gamma glutamyl transferase activities and road traffic accidents, but not alcohol concentrations or previous convictions. GGT levels remained abnormal through the period of driving licence suspension (Dunbar et al. 1985). Many of these drivers were known by their family doctors to have alcohol problems.

Comparing these results with Finnish studies indicates that random breath-testing in Finland deters social drinkers and detects problem drinkers. The latter are more likely to be driving in the morning traffic when vulnerable road users such as children are about, and are more likely to be detected by random breath-testing than any other police activity.

The presence of problem drinkers among the drink-driving population was officially recognised by the British Government in 1983. These 'high-risk offenders' are defined as drivers with two convictions at 200mg / 100ml or who refused to give specimens. As such, they are regarded as having a medical disability which affects their driving, and their licence is not restored until they can demonstrate that their drinking is under control. As the result of research in Tayside, the government has now accepted that the criteria should be widened to include any driver with one offence over 200mg/100ml or repeat offenders. This will mean that 40,000 offenders a year are referred to the Medical Adviser of the Driver and Vehicle Licensing Authority.

TREATMENT PROGRAMMES FOR CONVICTED PROBLEM DRINKING DRIVERS

Until recently, treatment programmes for problem drinking drivers were limited to pioneering work in Hampshire and the West Midlands in England. As a result of the success of these programmes and a review of the federal German scheme, the British government intends to introduce a national network of treatment programmes for offenders as part of the Road Traffic Law Reform Bill (HMSO 1989). Retraining and rehabilitation programmes will be run by the Probation Service in England and Wales and the Social Work Departments in Scotland.

CONCLUSION

There has been progress in controlling alcohol-impaired driving in Britain over the last decade. A number of initiatives were proposed in 1976, but politicians chose to introduce the least controversial and least effective of these measures. A similar process is recurring in the 1990s, but the difference is the higher public awareness of the issue and greater pressure for effective action. In particular, pressure on government to introduce random breath-testing is strong.

REFERENCES

Aberg, L., Engdahl, S. and Nilsson, E. (1986) TFB Report no. 12, Swedish Transport Research Board Stockholm.

Arthurson, R.M. (1985) 'Evaluation of random testing in New South Wales, Australia', Traffic Authority of New South Wales, 24–31.

Department of Transport (1988) *Road Safety*, London, HMSO.

Dunbar, J.A., Martin, B.T., Devgun, M.S., Haggart, J. Ogston, S.A. (1983) 'Problem drinking among drunk drivers', *British Medical Journal* 286, 1319–22.

Dunbar, J.A., Ogston, S.A., Ritchie, A., Devgun, M.S., Haggart J. and Martin, B.T. (1985) 'Are problem drinkers dangerous drivers? An investigation of arrest for drinking and driving, serum gammaglutamyl transpeptidase activities blood alcohol concentrations in road traffic accidents: the Tayside Safe Driving Project', *British Medical Journal* 290, 827–30.

Dunbar, J.A., Penttila, A. and Pakkarainen, J. (1987) 'Drinking and driving: the success of random breath testing in Finland', *British Medical Journal* 295, 101–3.

HMSO (1989) *The Road User and the Law: The Government's Proposals for Reform of the Road Traffic Law*, London, HMSO.

National Opinion Polls (1989) *Attitudes to Random Breath Testing*, London, NOP.

Peacock, C. (1992) 'International policies to curb alcohol-impaired driving: A review', *International Journal of the Addictions* 27, 187–208.

Trafiknykterhetsbrott Forslag (1970) *SOK 1970* 61, 373–4.

13. Alcohol and young offenders: Off the mystery train?

STEVE BALDWIN

INTRODUCTION

Until the 1990s, the development of services for young offenders in Scotland was haphazard and piecemeal. Despite the possibilities for centralisation and coordination following shifts in legislation, it is only recently that service provision has reflected any real cohesive reformism.

Such reforms have developed from thrusts both in the statutory sector and within non-government services in local Councils on Alcohol. In particular, there have been concerted efforts to develop alternatives to custodial sentencing options for young adult offenders with early-stage drinking problems. Also, in the statutory sector, there have been parallel developments in some courts, police forces, Social Work Departments and prisons. Although no single explanation exists for these different trends, their combined effects have produced a unique opportunity for major structural reforms in the Scottish criminal justice system at the beginning of the 1990s.

The separate strands of some of these new developments will be traced from their origins in eight towns and cities.

DUNDEE

In 1979, the first attempts were made to provide non-custodial sentencing alternatives for young male offenders aged between seventeen and twenty-nine. Prolonged discussions with local stakeholders, including the Social Work Department, the Sheriff Courts and the local Council on Alcohol, produced the first Alcohol Education Course (AEC) in 1981 (Robertson and Heather 1982). This AEC was designed to provide information and skills-education to assist young adult offenders to reform their problem behaviour. Although this course was not evaluated, it provided a landmark for subsequent service development in Scotland.

In 1985, a new evaluation project was started in Dundee. This venture aimed to develop new services for young drinking offenders, via collaboration between non-government sector services and the local courts. The Dundee initiative formed part of a larger national project to examine the effectiveness of AECs (Baldwin 1991; Baldwin et al. 1991a).

These services have endured into the 1990s, with a commitment from the local Council on Alcohol to expand their remit into other cities. Also, in 1987, a precedent was established between the agency and the District and Sheriff courts; a payment of £25 was made for each interview completed by agency workers. This principle has since been adopted elsewhere in other Councils on Alcohol in Scotland.

PERTH

Since the beginning of the 1980s, a service has been available from Alcoholics Anonymous (AA) in Perth prison for offenders who wish to stop drinking completely. This abstinence-based approach may be of value to some offenders; however, for many teenage and young adult offenders, abstinence will be an unrealistic goal (Baldwin 1990). Such AA services, based on weekly group meetings run by older ex-drinkers, are common in Scottish jails.

Elsewhere in Perth, a parallel referral scheme was established in 1986 between the Sheriff Courts and the Tayside Council on Alcohol. A full range of services was not yet available, however, and contact with clients was limited to brief screening interviews (Baldwin et al. 1992). Subsequently, in 1988, AECs were provided for young adults with drink-related offending; this service has continued into the 1990s, with the more recent involvement of Perth Social Work Department (Baldwin 1991).

FORFAR

In Forfar, services have been provided by the Social Work Department since 1982. With the cooperation of the Sheriff Court, referrals have been accepted via a probation order for young offenders to attend an AEC. The content of the AEC has been based on information-provision rather than skills training.

This work completed in Forfar has formed part of a larger project to measure the relative impact of an assessment-only control group (Baldwin 1991). These services are well established in the county of Angus (Baldwin, Ford and Heather 1986; Baldwin et al. 1986; Ward and Baldwin 1990). The therapeutic impact of 'information-only' education has been challenged, however (Baldwin 1991). The value of information-provision as a form of 'alcohol education' has been discussed in Chapter 8.

Near Forfar, at Noranside Young Offenders Institution, the first controlled effectiveness evaluation in the UK of a pre-release AEC was completed in 1987. This study attempted to measure the impact of a skills-based AEC on drinking and offending behaviour. At fifteen-month follow-up interviews, changes in these two dependent variables were recorded among males aged between seventeen and twenty-four (Baldwin et al. 1991b).

ABERDEEN

The local Council on Alcohol has provided a reliable service for young offenders aged between seventeen and twenty-nine; these referrals have been accepted both from the courts and from the Social Work Department. Although these services have not been developed in the context of an evaluation strategy, there has been consistent local uptake.

DUMBARTON

The Dumbarton Council on Alcohol has been involved in service provision with young adult offenders since 1981. During this time, non-government workers have provided one-to-one counselling services for offenders referred from the District Courts.

This work has been described via post-hoc reporting of a cohort of young offenders who completed individual alcohol education programmes between 1981 and 1986 (Collins and Tate 1988). These findings have provided some support for the provision of programmes for individual offender-clients, as well as the more usual provision in groups.

RENFREW

A range of services has been made available for young adult offenders at the Renfrew Council on Alcohol. Using a comparative treatment design, offender clients have been offered one of several different interventions.

Individual offenders have been given one-to-one counselling, minimal intervention (eg bibliotherapy) or a full AEC. This project is likely to inform much subsequent service development in Strathclyde.

EDINBURGH

In the capital city, alcohol education has previously been available in Saughton jail. This has been group-based treatment provided by Alcoholics Anonymous and by local Councils on Alcohol; the impact of the work by Scottish jails is, however, unknown.

In collaboration with the Social Work Department and the Sheriff Courts, the Scottish Association for the Care and Resettlement of Offenders (SACRO) has developed a pilot project since the beginning of 1991 (Sinclair 1991). Although this initiative has not yet reported outcome data, initial investment from local stakeholders has been very high. With the cooperation of managers from both statutory and non-statutory services, new provision has been established for drinking offenders, involving the delivery of group-based AECs.

GLASGOW

The Glasgow Council on Alcohol (GCA) has worked closely with the District Courts to provide non-custodial sentencing alternatives for young drinking offenders. This project has been formalised as a diversion scheme within the criminal justice system (Allan and Cuthbert 1990). This service has not been evaluated, however. Diversion schemes have featured on the national agenda for more than a decade, (Erikson 1984). Also based at the GCA, a parallel service was established in 1987 for adult offenders aged between seventeen and twenty-nine. Referrals were accepted from the District Courts for young offenders to attend an AEC via a deferred sentence. Results from this study were inconclusive due to institutional problems in establishing the court service (Baldwin 1991). Some support was obtained for the provision of behavioural AECs for drinking offenders (Baldwin et al. 1991d).

In collaboration with several statutory and non-government agencies, the Scottish Council on Alcohol (SCA) initiated a pioneering prison-based project in 1990. For the first time, an alcohol service was located inside a prison as a policy initiative (Allan and Cuthbert 1990). The work of the SCA is described in Chapter 15. The Barlinnie Addiction Project (BAP) was thus established to offer offenders an opportunity to receive alcohol and drug education while in prison. BAP has been unique in Europe, and has also generated considerable interest elsewhere in the UK. Although the project has not been restricted specifically to young offenders, much of the service uptake has been from young substance abusers below the age of thirty (Small 1991).

Also based in Glasgow, the ADAPT project has been in operation since 1990. This venture has been designed to provide young substance abusers with an opportunity to attend an intensive education daytime programme. With a strong influence from Strathclyde Social Work Department, ADAPT has encouraged the referral of young adults with substance use problems to attend an intensive treatment programme (Walker 1991). Although the project has not yet reported outcome data, there has been considerable interest from the criminal justice system in Glasgow. The true impact of such intensive programming (e.g. fifty to sixty hours) with young adult substance abusers remains unknown.

NATIONAL INITIATIVES

One outcome of this rapid development of local projects has been an increased interest at national level for a co-ordinated response to the challenge provided by drinking offenders. It has historically been difficult to ensure an equitable and rational distribution of non-institutionalised mental health services across both urban and rural sites (Barker 1990). Nonetheless, several developments have indicated a more cohesive response. In 1989, the Scottish Prison Service, in collaboration with the Scottish Council on Alcohol, initiated a Scotland-wide training programme. Since January 1991, pre-release AECs have been provided in Young Offenders Institutions as a central policy initiative (Baldwin et al. 1989). Although outcome data have not yet been made available, this new development has generated much interest in the rest of the UK, and elsewhere in Europe.

Other training initiatives have remained as planning proposals without full implementation. At the national level, a full commitment will be required to link firmly the twenty-five non-government Councils on Alcohol to the criminal justice system at the local level.

FUTURE DIRECTIONS

Several problems remain unresolved in the national provision of services for teenage and young adult drinking offenders. First, services for female offenders remain woefully inadequate. Although there have been many innovative service developments for male offenders in Scotland during the 1980s, generally these benefits have not been shared by female offenders. Both in institutions and in local neighbourhood settings, much work is still required to assist women drinking offenders to gain access to quality services (Macmillan and Baldwin 1992).

Similarly, for offenders from ethnic minority groups, the spectrum of available services has been predictably narrow during the 1980s. In Scotland, black and Asian client offenders have received almost no local generic services and no special needs services. Uptake among local Councils on Alcohol has become a point of shame for staff, who frequently operate in the absence of policy to inform such service development.

Second, the general level of special needs provision has been slow to develop in Scotland. Most young offenders receive alcohol education programmes in a specialist service (e.g. Council on Alcohol) which will congregate and segregate clients in groups. Attendance on court-referred AECs at such agencies may further stigmatise clients who are already at risk from previous contact with the criminal justice system. Ideally, offender-clients should receive any 'alcohol education' in educational settings (e.g. at night school in a College of Further Education). The negative effects of inappropriate provision of specialist services in place of better targeted special needs services are well-known (Baldwin 1987).

Third, the need remains to provide an accessible range of quality services for young drinking offenders in different parts of Scotland. The equitable distribution of such services to client-offenders who typically reflect transient and mobile lifestyles will be a continuing challenge during the 1990s.

Hence, although urban services for young adult male offenders have become well established during the 1980s, there remains much development work ahead in the field of service design.

SUMMARY

There is much work already completed to generate national pride in Scotland. Both educational/treatment materials and staff training packages have been 'exported' for subsequent use in England, Wales and Australia (Baldwin and Macmillan 1992). Nonetheless, to reduce further the levels of problem drinking and offending behaviour in the 1990s, additional commitments are required at policy level, with parallel investments in service development and national evaluation of programmes.

REFERENCES

Allan, C. and Cuthbert, J. (1990) 'Glasgow Council on Alcohol: trends and developments in a community-based voluntary organization', *Health Bulletin* 48, 238–42.
Baldwin, S. (1987) 'From community to neighbourhoods – 1', *Disability, Handicap and Society* 2, 41–59.
Baldwin, S. (1991) *Alcohol Education and Young Offenders: Medium and Short-Term Effects*, New York, Springer-Verlag.
Baldwin, S. (1992) *Alcohol Education and Offenders*, London, Batsford Academic.
Baldwin, S., Ford, I. and Heather, N. (1986) 'Drink and Crime I', *Community Care* 16–17.
Baldwin, S. and Macmillan, J. (1992) 'Down to zero: preliminary report on brief interventions with drinking offenders in UK magistrates courts', (in preparation).
Baldwin, S., Wilson, M., Lancaster, A., Allsop, D., McGowan, T., McMurran, M. and Hodge, J. (1989) *Ending Offending 2: An Alcohol Training Resource Pack for use with Young Offenders*, Glasgow, Scottish Council on Alcohol.
Baldwin, S., Heather, N., Lawson, A., Robertson, I., Mooney, J. and Braggins, F. (1991a) 'Comparison of effectiveness: behavioural and talk-based alcohol education courses for young offenders', *Behavioural Psychotherapy* 19, 157–71.
Baldwin, S., Heather, N., Lawson, A., Gama, S., Greer, C., Robertson, I., Ward, M. and Williams, A., (1991b) 'Alcohol education courses for pre-release young offenders', *Behavioural Psychotherapy*, 19, 321–33.
Baldwin, S., Heather, N., Lawson, A., Greer, C. and Gamba, S. (1992) 'Alcohol education courses for offenders: impact of information provision' (in preparation).
Baldwin, S., Heather, N., Lawson, A., Greer, C., McCluskey, S. and Cuthbert, J., (1991c) 'Alcohol education courses in urban courts: a replication study' (in preparation).
Berker, P., (1991) 'Community care: myths and fairy tale wishes, a Scottish impression of care in the community', *Architecture and Behaviour* 6, 233–44.
Collins, S. and Tate, D. (1988) 'Alcohol related offenders and a voluntary organization in a Scottish community', *Howard Journal* 27, 44–57.
Erikson, P.G. (1984) 'Diversion – a panacea for delinquency? Lessons from the Scottish experience', *Youth and Society* 16, 29–45.
Macmillan, J. and Baldwin, S. (1992) 'What's good for the goose: preliminary report of alcohol consumption in a women's jail', (in preparation).
Robertson, I. and Heather, N. (1982) 'Alcohol education courses for offenders: a preliminary study', *Alcohol and Alcoholism* 17, 32–8.
Small, J. (1991) personal communication.

Sinclair, J. (1991) personal communication.

Walker, B., (1991) personal communication.

Ward, M. and Baldwin, S. (1990) 'Alcohol education courses (AECs) as a court disposal: a preliminary examination of effectiveness', *Alcohol Treatment Quarterly* 7, 123–33.

14. Minimal intervention with problem drinkers

ALASDAIR MURRAY

In the introduction to their comprehensive review of the alcohol treatment literature, Miller and Hester (1980) highlighted a number of questions which are relevant to those involved in the planning and delivery of alcohol problem services: namely, does alcohol treatment work and if so, who benefits from what kind of treatment under which conditions? Although some progress has been made towards answering these questions (Miller and Hester 1986), the issues are more complex than originally conceived. For one thing, treatment outcome is determined by an interaction among client characteristics, the treatment offered and life events occurring before, during and after intervention. Moreover, the trend towards early treatment and prevention strategies has considerably increased the range of problems now considered to be legitimate targets for intervention (Heather 1986). Consequently, the need for high-quality outcome research which adequately addresses such questions remains as pertinent as ever (see Chapter 21).

Interest in providing brief, cost-effective yet efficacious treatments has been prompted by two comparatively recent developments. Firstly, evaluation studies have failed to demonstrate a significant superiority of traditionally intensive therapies over less intensive alternatives. In reviewing the influence of both the length of treatment and the treatment setting (i.e. inpatient versus outpatient), Miller and Hester (1986) concluded that more intensive approaches are not necessarily better. However, they cautioned that intensity effects cannot be considered in isolation from the content of the treatment on offer.

An oft-cited example of comparative research investigating this issue is that of Orford and Edwards (1977). The study sample comprised two groups of married male alcohol dependents who were randomly allocated to one of two interventions: either conventional treatment or brief advice. The treatment goal in both instances was total abstinence.

Following an initial assessment, during which the male alcohol dependents and their wives were interviewed, each couple was randomly assigned to the 'Treatment' or to the 'Advice' group. Those in the former were provided with a broad-spectrum approach comprising a selection of possible treatments including detoxification, citrated calcium carbimide, introduction to Alcoholics Anonymous, individual counselling, joint marital counselling and social work support for practical problems relating to employment, housing, finance and the courts. If outpatient treatment proved ineffective, the husband was offered inpatient treatment with an estimated duration of six weeks.

By contrast, the couples in the Advice group were seen for a single, brief, joint session in which it was made clear that responsibility for overcoming the problem lay in their own hands and that the clinic would not offer further appointments, although a social worker would visit on a monthly basis to collect follow-up data. Finally, the couple were provided with some personalised advice on how to cope with the problem by relying solely on their own resources.

At a one-year follow-up, there were no significant differences on measures of drinking behaviour. With a number of important qualifications, the conclusion drawn from this study was that the Advice regime produced as good results as the more intensive Treatment intervention. However, rather than promoting a nihilistic attitude towards therapy, the authors made a plea for existing treatments to be improved upon. Nevertheless, the study provoked some retaliation in the form of a defence of existing intensive inpatient programmes (McLellan et al. 1982; Blume 1983).

In a follow-up of sixty-five couples from the original cohort, two years after intake into the study, twenty-six men were classified as having a 'good' outcome according to drinking-pattern data received from both husband and wife (Orford, Oppenheimer and Edwards 1976). Of these, eleven were abstinent or essentially abstinent and ten were drinking in an acceptable fashion. Neither age nor problem chronicity were predictive of abstinence as against moderate drinking. However, those who abstained were more likely to have shown signs of physical dependence and 'loss of control' (i.e. gamma alcoholics) at intake and to have been allocated to the 'Treatment' group. By contrast, those who proceeded to control their drinking during the second year were more likely to have low symptom counts and to have received brief advice. It would therefore seem that the original conclusion was premature and that there is indeed a place for intensive treatments in the management of some, but not all, drinking problems.

Further support for this view has been forthcoming from a recently reported study by Chick et al. (1988). At a two-year follow-up of those clients attending an alcohol problems clinic who received 'extended' treatment, there was less evidence of alcohol-related harm than among those who had received either of two variants of brief advice. Research efforts, therefore, might more usefully return to matching individual clients to the most appropriate treatment at primary and secondary as well as tertiary levels of intervention.

The second important stimulus to the development of brief interventions has stemmed from the growth in demand for services. This has, in turn, enforced an increased appreciation that therapeutic and economic resources are finite and consequently have to be utilised to best advantage. Hawks (1981), albeit in a different context, aptly characterised the dilemma for clinical practitioners: namely, how to meet the growing demand for assistance from individuals who do not yet exhibit the classic signs and symptoms of psychological or behavioural distress but who nevertheless perceive some problem (possibly early-stage problem drinkers), while allowing sufficient time for the proper assessment and treatment of individuals with more intransigent difficulties.

One way in which those skilled in psychological therapies have attempted to cope with vastly increased demands in other areas of mental health is by disseminating therapeutic techniques to other non-specialist professional groups and also more directly to the consumer via a range of written materials. Glasgow and Rosen (1978) distinguished three ways in which so-called 'bibliotherapy' (i.e. the use of literature to facilitate therapy) could be utilised. In the context of literature which provides information about treatment strategies, as opposed to works of a fictional or purely factual nature, Glasgow and Rosen's classification might be understood by the following three illustrative examples:

SELF-ADMINISTERED THERAPY

Normally, the individual would select the material in the absence of therapist involvement, as, for example, when an anxious person buys a book for personal use on stress management from a bookshop or borrows such material from a public library.

MINIMAL THERAPIST CONTACT

The main thrust of this form of intervention comprises the dissemination of written information under the direction of a professional or other specialist. The recipient would usually assume responsibility for implementing and evaluating the success of the treatment, and any follow-up would lie at the discretion of the professional. An example might be a GP providing a smoking-cessation booklet to a smoker suffering from a respiratory complaint.

THERAPIST-ADMINISTERED TREATMENT

In this instance, the provision of written material is offered primarily to supplement more intensive therapist contact. The aim is often to provide the recipient with a thorough understanding of the techniques being utilised within therapy. Therapists engaging in cognitive-behavioural treatments often aim to reinforce what has been discussed within a session with explanatory or illustrative materials, or will include home study as a means of preparing clients for future sessions. Ongoing therapist contact is, however, considered to be an essential element of treatment.

Heather (1986) considers a treatment intervention to be 'minimal' if it entails a significantly smaller amount of professional time and/or resources than is typically employed in conventional treatment practice. The term 'minimal' is therefore a relative rather than an absolute term and is presumably in some way dependent upon the client group engaged in treatment. For example, a minimal treatment strategy with low-dependence problem drinkers in a primary care setting may well differ from that employed with more severely dependent drinkers seen within a specialist alcohol treatment centre. Nevertheless, the use of self-help manuals, either in the course of self-administered therapy or in conjunction with minimal therapist contact, as described above, clearly falls within the bounds of a minimal or brief intervention.

Over the last ten to fifteen years, there has been a rapid increase in both the range and the availability of self-help materials, as publishers have become aware of the commercial opportunities. Problems addressed include panic attacks, poor assertion skills, sexual dysfunction, depression, obesity, smoking, tranquilliser dependence and problem drinking. From the compliance literature, there is good evidence that, when used as an adjunct to therapist contact, written materials can act as an aide-mémoire to reinforce what has taken place within therapy (Eraker, Kirscht and Becker 1979). However, as Turvey (1985) has rightly cautioned, much of the self-help literature has not been adequately validated and, consequently, the precise contribution of such material to the outcome remains largely unclear. This may be due partly to the obvious difficulties in evaluating materials which are completely self-selected and self-administered and partly to the large number of client, therapy and setting variables which require to be controlled. Issues such as these necessarily make comparisons between different outcome studies difficult.

In the context of problem drinking, however, some attempt has been made to validate self-help materials. In the USA, Miller and his colleagues have developed and evaluated a manual based on the principles of behavioural self-management theory (Miller and Muñoz 1976; Miller and Taylor 1980; Miller and Baca 1983). The conclusions drawn from these studies were that ten sessions of therapist contact, utilising the principles of behavioural self-control training (i.e. functional analysis, stimulus control, self-monitoring, limit-setting, blood-alcohol discrimination training, self-reinforcement and alcohol education), whether offered individually or in a group setting, provided no advantage over an initial assessment and provision with a self-help manual and self-monitoring cards. As a 'no-treatment-control' was not utilised, Miller points out that it is not possible to conclude that the outcome was significantly superior to that which might have occurred due to spontaneous remission. However, circumstantial support in favour of a superior outcome could be drawn from other studies in which untreated subjects reported improvement rates well below that obtained by Miller (Miller and Hester 1980). However, a further criticism levelled by Carey and Maisto (1985) is that no attempt was made to demonstrate to what extent, if at all, subjects receiving the self-help manual had in fact made use of the material and had subsequently utilised self-control strategies to reduce their consumption of alcohol.

Similar self-help material has been developed and validated on samples of Scottish drinkers (Robertson and Heather 1983; Robertson and Heather 1985). Heather, Whitton and Robertson (1986) compared a group of problem drinkers who received a self-help manual to one receiving a booklet offering general educational information and advice. In an attempt to enhance the external validity of their study, initial and follow-up assessments were carried out by postal questionnaire or by telephone contact. Consequently, there was no face-to-face contact with therapists. At a six-month follow-up, those who had received the manual showed a significantly greater reduction in their previous week's consumption of alcohol than those who received the information booklet. This superiority was paralleled by significantly greater improvements on variables measuring physical health and wellbeing and in control over drinking problems. Also of some interest was the trend for those contacted by telephone to show greater mean reductions in alcohol consumption than those responding by post. These findings were once again confirmed in a reduced follow-up sample at one year (Heather et al. 1987a). However, a subsequent study, while demonstrating that a higher proportion of control subjects were drinking above recommended limits compared to those receiving the behaviourally-based self-help manual, failed to find any additional advantage as a result of supplementary telephone contact (Heather, Kissoon-Singh and Fenton 1990).

While recognising the difficulties inherent in attempts to validate materials in a natural (i.e. non-treatment) setting, it is important to bear in mind the methodologies employed in these various studies before attempting to extrapolate the findings to other settings and/or populations. For example, a number of studies have recruited subjects who responded to newspaper advertisements offering assistance to those concerned about their drinking (Miller and Taylor 1980; Miller, Taylor and West 1980; Heather, Whitton and Robertson 1986; Skutle and Berg 1987). It might reasonably be assumed that the respondents, having by definition acknowledged some concern about their drinking, were already motivated to implement strategies for change. This group may very well be quite different from e.g. general hospital inpatients or individuals attending their family doctor, whose potential or actual drinking problems have been identified in the course of routine screening. Indeed, Heather et al. (1987b) found no significant differences in reduction of alcohol consumption among three groups of patients (assessment-only controls, simple advice and self-help manual) in a study conducted in a general practice setting. One possible explanation for this finding might be that, even if patients themselves were aware of alcohol-related difficulties, they may not yet have been prepared to modify their alcohol intake.

Nevertheless, bearing in mind any constraints imposed by subject self-selection, there is now good evidence that self-help materials, based on behavioural principles, are an effective means of assisting individuals to reduce their consumption of alcohol. However, although Heather and colleagues made some attempt to establish whether those receiving the manual had found it interesting and/or useful, little has been known until recently about which parts of what is essentially a multi-component package are effective in fostering reduced alcohol consumption.

Savage, Hollin and Hayward (1990) reversed the order of presentation of a self-help package based heavily on that of Robertson and Heather (1986). Essentially, half of a sample of twenty-six media-recruited problem drinkers received the health education component first, followed by the self-management component four weeks later. The remainder received the self-management part first,followed, once again after a four-week interval, by the health education section. Although both groups showed a significant reduction in alcohol consumption at the four-week follow-up point, those receiving the self-management material first showed greater improvement than those receiving the material in reverse order. Savage et al. (1990) discuss this finding in terms of Prochaska and Diclemente's (1982) model of change and suggest that it may be important to match the therapeutic response to the drinker's readiness for change.

So far, this discussion of minimal intervention has focused heavily on the use of self-help materials in community settings. However, over the past twenty-five years, there has been a growing appreciation that general hospital populations comprise a higher percentage of problem drinkers and alcohol dependents than does the general population

(Green 1965; Nolan 1965; Quinn and Johnston 1976; Jarman and Kellet 1979; Jariwalla, Adams and Hore 1979; Corrigan, Webb and Unwin 1986). Similar findings have been evident from surveys of outpatient clinics (Persson and Magnusson 1987). While many of these studies have been criticised for their failure to operationalise adequately terms such as 'alcoholic' or 'alcohol-related problems' (McIntosh 1982), evidence supporting an association between alcohol consumption and damage to health is available from epidemiological studies (Dyer et al. 1980; Shaper et al. 1981; Marmot et al. 1981). Taking this evidence, it would seem reasonable to consider general hospitals to be an appropriate setting in which to carry out screening for evidence of both established and incipient drinking problems and to offer both primary and secondary prevention programmes.

In Edinburgh, Chick, Lloyd and Crombie (1985) screened admissions to male medical wards. Twenty-two per cent were considered to be problem drinkers who had not previously received treatment for a drinking problem and who met at least two of the following criteria: having some social support in the form of spouse or close friend; living with one other person; or employed within the last six months. Those consenting to participate in the study were allocated either to an assessment-only control condition or to an intervention group. The latter received structured counselling on lifestyle and health issues, which included a cost-benefit analysis of drinking habits and a booklet providing information and advice on drinking problems. The general aim of the intervention was to assist subjects to achieve problem-free drinking, although abstinence was the agreed goal for a minority.

At twelve months' follow-up, both groups had significantly reduced their mean weekly alcohol consumption from that reported on entering the study. However, those who had received counselling also showed a significant improvement in scores for problems related to alcohol and gamma glutamyl transpeptidase activity. Moreover, significantly more of those in the intervention group, compared with controls, were rated as 'definitely improved'. While the overall superiority of the group receiving a single session of counselling is of interest, this study raises several important questions. In particular, what explanation might there be to account for the control group reducing their consumption from a mean of sixty-nine units at intake to a mean of thirty-five units at follow-up? (A 'unit' of alcohol is equivalent to a single public bar measure of spirits or to a single glass of wine or to half a pint of 'normal' strength beer, lager, cider or stout.) Each unit contains approximately one centilitre of pure alcohol.

The phenomenon of reduced drinking in control samples from intake to follow-up is one which has been described in a number of other studies (e.g. Heather, Whitton and Robertson 1986; Heather, Kissoon-Singh and

Fenton 1990). Elvy, Wells and Baird (1988) reported that their twelve-month follow-up interview with control subjects, who were drawn from a sample of surgical and orthopaedic patients, seemed to serve as a form of intervention since this group showed further gains when a second follow-up was carried out six months later. While regression to the mean effects cannot be discounted, it seems plausible that detailed enquiries into alcohol consumption and alcohol-related problems may in themselves constitute a minimal intervention. If this conclusion can be substantiated, the value of conducting alcohol screening in both primary and secondary health-care settings will take on a renewed importance. Not only can those individuals with existing and emergent problems be identified, but screening may also take on a preventive and possibly also a therapeutic function. However, Ritson (1986) has wisely cautioned against the uncritical adoption of these apparently simple treatment strategies, particularly as much remains to be understood about the timing, presentation and content of what are, in practice, a heterogeneous range of techniques. There is a danger that the inappropriate application of minimal interventions may ultimately result in potentially useful techniques becoming discredited. Oversimplification of complex processes is not in anyone's interest, especially if it results in poor-quality services.

REFERENCES

Blume, S.E (1983) 'Is alcoholism treatment worthwhile?', *Bulletin of the New York Academy of Medicine* 59, 171–80.

Carey, K.B. and Maisto, S.A. (1985) 'A review of the use of self-control techniques in the treatment of alcohol abuse', *Cognitive Therapy and Research* 9, 235–51.

Chick, J., Lloyd, G. and Crombie, E. (1985) 'Counselling problem drinkers in medical wards: a controlled study', *British Medical Journal* 290, 965–7.

Chick, J., Ritson, E B., Connaughton, J., Stewart, A. and Chick, J. (1988) 'Advice versus extended treatment for Alcoholism: a controlled study', *British Journal of Addiction* 83, 159–70.

Corrigan, G.V., Webb, M.G.T. and Unwin, A.R. (1986) 'Alcohol dependence among general medical inpatients', *British Journal of Addiction* 81, 237–46.

Dyer, A.R., Stamler, J., Paul, D., Lepper, M., Shekelle, R.B., 'McKean, H. and Garside, D. (1980) 'Alcohol consumption and 17-year mortality in the Chicago Western Electric Company study', *Preventive Medicine* 9, 78–9.

Elvy, G.A., Wells, J.E. and Baird, K.A. (1988) 'Attempted referral as intervention for problem drinking in the general hospital', *British Journal of Addiction* 83, 83–9.

Eraker, S.A., Kirscht, J.P. and Becker, M.H. (1984) Understanding and improving patient compliance', *Annals of Internal Medicine* 100, 258–68.

Glasgow, R.E. and Rosen, G.M. (1978) 'Behavioural bibliotherapy: a review of self-help behaviour therapy manuals', *Psychological Bulletin* 85, 1–23.

Green, J.R. (1965) 'The incidence of alcoholism in patients admitted to medical wards of a public hospital', *Medical Journal of Australia* 1, 465–6.

Hawks, D. (1981) 'The dilemma of clinical practice: surviving as a clinical psychologist in the primary care setting' in McPherson, I. and Sutton, A. (eds) *Reconstructing Psychological Practice*, London, Croom Helm, 11–20.

Heather, N. (1986) 'Change without therapists: the use of self-help manuals by problem drinkers', in Miller, W.R. and Heather, N. (eds) *Treating Addictive Behaviors*, New York, Plenum, 331–59.

Heather, N., Whitton, B. and Robertson, I. (1986) 'Evaluation of a self-help manual for media-recruited problem-drinkers: Six-month follow-up results', *British Journal of Clinical Psychology* 25, 19–34.

Heather, N., Robertson, I., McPherson, B., Allsop, S. and Fulton, A. (1987a) 'Effectiveness of a controlled drinking self-help manual: One-year follow-up results', *British Journal of Clinical Psychology*, 26, 279–87.

Heather, N., Kissoon-Singh, J. and Fenton, G.W. (1990) 'Assisted natural recovery from alcohol problems: effects of a self-help manual with and without supplementary telephone contact', *British Journal of Addiction* 85, 1177–85.

Heather, N., Campion, P., Neville, R.G. and MacCabe, D. (1987b) 'Evaluation of a controlled drinking minimal intervention for problem drinkers in general practice (the DRAMS scheme)', *Journal of the Royal College of General Practioners* 37, 358–63.

Jarman, H.B. and Kellett, J.M. (1979) 'Alcoholism in the general hospital', *British Medical Journal* 2, 469–72.

Jariwalla, A.G., Adams, P.H. and Hore, B.D. (1979) 'Alcohol and acute general medical admissions to hospital', *Health Trends* 11, 95–7.

Marmot, M.G., Rose, G., Shipley, M.J. and Thomas, B.J. (1981) 'Alcohol and mortality: a J-shaped curve', *Lancet* 1, 580–3.

McIntosh, I. (1982) 'Alcohol-related disabilities in general hospital patients: a critical assessment of the evidence', *International Journal of the Addictions* 17, 609–39.

McLellan, A.T., Luborsky, L., O'Brien, C.P., Woody, G.E. and Drulev, K.A. (1982) 'Is treatment for substance abuse effective?', *Journal of the American Medical Association*, 247, 1423–8.

Miller, W.R. and Baca, L.M. (1983) 'Two-year follow-up of bibliotherapy and therapist-directed controlled drinking training for problem drinkers', *Behavior Therapy* 14, 441–8.

Miller, W.R. and Hester, R.K. (1980) 'Treating the problem drinker: Modern approaches', in Miller, W.R. (ed.) *The Addictive Behaviors: Treatment of Alcoholism, Drug Abuse, Smoking and Obesity*, Oxford, Pergamon, 111–41.

Miller, W.R. and Hester, R.K. (1986) 'The effectiveness of alcoholism treatment: what research reveals', in Miller, W.R. and Heather, N. (eds) *Treating Addictive Behaviors: Processes of Change*, New York, Plenum, 121–74.

Miller, W.R. and Munoz, R.F. (1976) *How to Control Your Drinking*, Englewood Cliffs, NJ, Prentice-Hall.

Miller, W.R. and Joyce, C.A. (1980) 'Relative effectiveness of bibliotherapy, individual and group self-control training in the treatment of problem drinkers', *Addictive Behaviors* 5, 13-24.

Miller, W.R., Taylor, C.A. and West, J.C. (1980) 'Focused versus broad-spectrum behavior therapy for problem drinkers', *Journal of Consulting and Clinical Psychology* 48, 590–601.

Nolan, J.P. (1965) 'Alcohol as a factor in the illness of university service patients', *American Journal of Medical Science* 249, 37–44.

Orford, J. and Edwards, G. (1977) *Alcoholism*, Maudsley Monograph no. 26, London, Oxford University Press.

Orford, J., Oppenheimer, E. and Edwards, G. (1976) 'Abstinence or control: the outcome for excessive drinkers two years after consultation', *Behaviour Research and Therapy* 14, 409–18.

Persson, J. and Magnusson P. (1987) 'Prevalence of excessive or problem drinkers amongst patients attending somatic outpatient clinics: a study of alcohol-related medical care', *British Medical Journal* 295, 467–72.

Prochaska, J.O. and Diclemente, C.C. (1982) 'Transtheoretical therapy: toward a more integrative model of change', *Psychotherapy: Theory, Research and Practice* 19, p. 276.

Quinn, M.A. and Johnston, R.V. (1976) 'Alcohol problems in acute male medical admissions', *Health Bulletin* 34, p. 253.

Ritson, E.B. (1986) 'Merits of single intervention', in Miller, W.K. and Heather, N. (eds) *Treating Addictive Behaviors: Processes of Change*, New York, Plenum, 375–87.

Robertson, I. and Heather, N. (1983) *So You Want To Cut Down Your Drinking? A self-help manual for controlled drinking*, Edinburgh, Scottish Health Education Group.

Robertson, I. and Heather, N. (1985) *So You Want To Cut Down Your Drinking? A self-help guide to sensible drinking*, Edinburgh, Scottish Health Education Group.

Robertson, I. and Heather, N. (1986) *Let's Drink to Your Health! A Self-Help Guide to Sensible Drinking*, Leicester, The British Psychological Society.

Savage, S.A., Hollin, C.R. and Hayward, A.J. (1990) 'Self-help manuals for problem drinking: The relative effects of their educational and therapeutic components', *British Journal of Clinical Psychology* 29, 373–82.

Shaper, A.G., Pocock, S.J., Walker, M., Cohen N.M., Wale, C.J. and Thomson, A.G. (1978) 'British Regional Heart Study: Cardiovascular risk factors in middle-aged men in 24 towns', *British Medical Journal* 283, 179–86.

Skutle, A. and Berg, G. (1987) 'Training in controlled drinking for early-stage problem drinkers', *British Journal of Addiction* 82, 493–501.

Turvey, A.A. (1985) 'Treatment manuals', in Watts, F.N. (ed.) *New Developments in Clinical Psychology*, London, British Psychological Society/Wiley.

PART III

SERVICE PROVISION

15. Scottish voluntary alcohol and drug services

DOUGLAS ALLSOP AND WILLY SLAVIN

ALCOHOL SERVICES

Historically, the provision of services to individuals experiencing alcohol problems goes back quite a long way in Scotland, although it is true to say that until the early 1960s the main provider of such services was Alcoholics Anonymous (AA). Alcoholics Anonymous remains a major provider of services to this day, with somewhere between 800 and 900 groups operating throughout Scotland.

Hostels have also been for many years a significant part of service delivery by the voluntary sector, and roughly one third of voluntary alcohol services could come under the heading of hostel provision. These now have a substantial range of approaches to alcohol problems, ranging from the traditional 'disease' concept of abstinence orientation through a number of projects where drinking is permitted, and also including projects where minimal intervention techniques are practised, with a view to total rehabilitation within society. There are also a number of supported accommodation projects linked in with alcohol agencies dealing with a wider client group, and one of the most interesting developments over the last few years has been the development by the voluntary sector of a range of initiatives coming under the aegis of one single agency.

Next to Alcoholics Anonymous, local Councils on Alcohol have been the fastest-growing part of the voluntary sector over the last fifteen to twenty years. These are autonomous local bodies, most with minimal full-time staff, all of which are affiliated to the national body, the Scottish Council on Alcohol.

The first Council on Alcohol in Scotland was set up in Glasgow in 1966 by three individuals who wished to see an alternative to AA in Scotland. Prior to the establishment of the Scottish Council on Alcohol in 1973, local Councils on Alcohol had also opened in Edinburgh, Aberdeen and Dundee.

It would certainly be true to say that, although run on different lines, the Councils on Alcohol in existence in the late 1960s and in the early 1970s were an alternative to AA in name only, since the disease concept of 'alcoholism' still reigned supreme.

After the establishment of the Scottish Council on Alcohol (SCA) in 1973, with support from the outset by the Scottish Office Home and Health Department, the development of a national network of local Councils on Alcohol really began. Throughout the 1970s and into the mid-1980s, there was a large expansion programme undertaken leading up to the current situation where there are twenty-six local Councils on Alcohol, with three more possibilities being actively considered at the time of writing. By the end of 1992 there will be a service available from a local Council on Alcohol in all parts of mainland Scotland, plus a substantial number of the island communities.

All of these local Councils on Alcohol are in themselves autonomous local bodies, but, by their affiliation to the SCA, plus the development of a National Training Scheme, the 'Network' concept has been developed.

The most important single factor in the development of what can be truly referred to as a 'National' approach was the development of a National Training Scheme for voluntary counsellors, which started in 1974. This was the work of Mr Iain Brown, a Senior Lecturer in Psychology at the University of Glasgow. The original concept was to take members of the general public, train them in basic counselling techniques, give them some knowledge of alcohol problems, attach them to local Councils on Alcohol and then expose them to clients. These basic principles still apply, although there is no doubt that the experience of this scheme, gained over some eighteen years, has led to a far higher level of expertise than was perhaps originally envisaged. The National Training Scheme has, since its inception, been very well supported by the Scottish Office Social Work Services Group, as well as many other commercial and industrial donors.

The first counselling course took place in 1975, and there followed some national courses in the years leading up to the formal adoption of the National Training Scheme in 1979. This adoption pledged all affiliated Councils to the acceptance of basic standards of service delivery, these being linked to the National Training Scheme, in that only counsellors who have been trained under this scheme will be used in service delivery with clients. The Scottish Council on Alcohol is now responsible for the recruitment, selection and training of counsellors on an annual basis, and in most years four or five training courses are run, all over Scotland, in order to provide the local Councils on Alcohol with the counselling strength which they require.

It is important to stress that the approach to alcohol problems by Councils on Alcohol, and obviously by the trained counsellors, does not recognise 'alcoholism' as a 'disease'. It would, however, be equally important to stress that many clients are counselled with the ultimate goal of abstinence for a variety of reasons. Councils on Alcohol reject exclusive reliance on any single method of responding to alcohol problems. In addition they do not accept that there is only ever one way to recovery. The view is taken that there is a large variety of drinking problems as well as problem drinkers, and that specific methods of approach must be developed to meet specific individual needs. The aim of counselling is that clients should eventually return to full community life without being dependent on alcohol, on continuing contact with an agency or indeed on any special group of people.

There are now 400 to 500 voluntary counsellors operating throughout Scotland, all of these being attached to one of the local Councils on Alcohol. The responsibility for formal support and supervision of such counsellors is a shared responsibility between the SCA and the local Councils involved. An Accreditation Scheme has been introduced as an acknowledgement of the development of expertise and skills over a number of years, and this is now a highly-prized feature of the training of counsellors.

The development of the National Training Scheme has been influenced to a considerable extent by changing circumstances and by an increasing acknowledgement of the fact that there is more to counselling than merely tackling the presenting problem. Over the last fifteen years, the typical client profile has changed markedly: the average age has dropped from the late forties to the late thirties, and the proportion of female clients has risen from one in six to near equality. Perhaps most importantly, many clients now present at a much earlier state of a developing problem than was the case previously. The voluntary counsellors do not restrict themselves solely to alcohol problems, since these seldom occur in isolation. They are able to tackle significant areas with which the client is experiencing difficulty, as well as tackling such matters as the development of other areas of life skills. Counsellors are, in fact, able and willing to take on the client as an individual, with special features and identifiable life problem areas.

The level of competence now associated with voluntary counsellors operating for local Councils on Alcohol is reflected in the growth of involvement with employers who use Councils on a regular basis to counsel employees referred under alcohol policies or employee assistance programmes. In 1990, the Scottish District Courts Association adopted a national scheme of referral for problem drinkers under deferred sentence. The Scottish Prisons Service has also set up a voluntary counselling service for problem drinkers within the confines of one of Scotland's major prisons. The response of the prison service to illegal drug problems is described in detail in Chapter 20.

Historically, there has been very little coordination or cooperation between agencies, who have tended to go their own way and 'do their own thing'. This is in the process of changing, due to a number of factors, one of which is the inauguration of 'Drinkwise' campaigns, the first of which was launched by the SCA in 1985. This event has subsequently been adopted in other parts of the United Kingdom. This type of high-profile campaign has encouraged many different services to become involved in some level of cooperation. The picture would appear to be developing further with the establishment of Local Alcohol Misuse Co-ordinating Committees on a regional basis throughout Scotland. These bodies were set up at the behest of the Scottish Office Home and Health Department, and are charged with the remit of organising and coordinating services on alcohol problems throughout their own regions. These are at a comparatively early stage of development, but the very wide-ranging membership is such that it is possible to foresee a level of coordination and cooperation through both the statutory and voluntary sector which will almost certainly result in a much more structured range and choice of services in the future.

The growth of problems arising from other addictive substances, both legal and illegal, over the last ten years or so has inevitably affected alcohol agencies to some extent, since alcohol misuse is often accompanied by polydrug use. While the main focus has remained on alcohol and will continue to do so, there has inevitably been some element of training in other drugs problems included in the National Training Scheme. However, separate drug agencies have been set up, and there is at the moment no formal linking of alcohol and drug services in the voluntary sector. This may well come about in the future, and certainly the two national bodies involved, the SCA and the Scottish Drugs Forum, have fairly strong links and their officials meet on a regular basis.

It is important to locate the more recent phenomenon of drug use within the wider context of alcohol (and also tobacco) in order to understand the nature of the response to the drug problem in Scotland in terms of services and the significant part that the voluntary sector has played in it. As noted in Chapter 1, Scottish drinking habits do not vary much from those of other parts of Britain. Even so, Scotland retains a distinctive drinking culture and in some areas has an atypically high proportion of abstainers. This has two consequences: first, ordinary people are often familiar with alcohol problems and are tolerant of them as part of daily life. Second, the solutions are seen to lie within society and to some extent within people themselves.

ILLICIT DRUGS SERVICES

During the 1960s and 1970s, there were few services for problem drug users in Scotland. With a few exceptions, these were hospital-based. The upsurge in illicit drug use which occurred during the late 1970s and early 1980s prompted a great increase in concern about drug use and misuse in Scotland.

The 1982 Advisory Council on the Misuse of Drugs Report on *Treatment and Rehabilitation* encouraged an idea of help that would be multidisciplinary and based in the community. In 1983, when central government money became available for the first time for drug projects, there is evidence that advisors in the Scottish Office were sympathetic to the view of the Advisory Council on the Misuse of Drugs (ACMD) Report, and the first round of grants (to the total of £500,000) favoured community-based applications. In Edinburgh, projects were funded in two housing estates, Muirhouse and Wester Hailes. In the former, a group of volunteers obtained premises for a drop-in centre in the local shopping centre, and in the latter the Community Council had set up a 'Hotline' in a council flat. Helplines were one of the most popular forms of community action in the drugs field. With the minimum of financial support and a great deal of voluntary effort, they were often instrumental in making the case for a full-time service. The drugs project in Greenock, for example, is still called Inverclyde Drugline.

In Glasgow, Strathclyde Regional Council in its 'Strategy for the 80s' had identified both housing estates and addiction services as priorities for support. Accordingly, Social Work Departments took the initiative in applying for funds for projects. In Easterhouse, this was planned in collaboration with the local Committee on Drug Abuse (ECODA) which had roots in the Easterhouse Festival Society. Possilpark Drug Project was housed in an alcohol rehabilitation centre.

In Dundee, there was still in 1982 a 'Heroin Clinic' at the Outpatients Department in Ninewells Hospital. But when central funding became available, although the psychiatrist remained in charge, the service was essentially demedicalised and sited in a well-known community centre (the Wishart). The only projects outside the three cities to receive central funding in 1984 had both strong links with the alcohol field and a large voluntary input, including an independent management which was representative of the local community: namely the Bridge Project in Ayr and the West Lothian Education Project in Livingston.

This relatively large injection of public funds into the drugs field – whether of central government money (now channelled through Area Health Boards) or of local authority grants (usually supervised by Regional Social Work Departments) marks an important distinction from the alcohol field. Not only is the drug problem much newer, the proposed solutions are much more 'finance-led'. Narcotics Anonymous, for example, hardly existed in Scotland, at least in a form to deal with the heroin 'epidemic' of the early 1980s. The age profile of those in difficulties with drugs was also younger (probably early to mid-twenties), and the problems, both legal and medical, were more acute (Home Office 1980-90; Plant and Plant 1991). This meant that although the policy was to encourage local voluntary initiatives, immediately there was pressure to provide a para-professional service, which was 'crisis-oriented'. There has not been the opportunity, for example, to build up a voluntary trained counsellor service as in the alcohol field. This is not to say that there do not exist purely voluntary projects without public funding. The Leith Drug Prevention Group, which has been in existence for almost a decade, and the more recent Calton Athletic in Glasgow are examples of projects well patronised by drug users which have not received grants. Until very recently, this was true also of the Family Support Groups, which are a classic example of self-help. Most of these exist in Glasgow, where they have formed themselves into an association and attracted Health Board funding for a development officer. Few such groups exist elsewhere in Scotland, although, in Edinburgh, SAFE (Support for Addiction for Families in Edinburgh) has received assistance with its 'Furnishare' Project to help users furnish their dwellings.

One disadvantage of opting for community-based projects has been the absence of rehabilitation projects serving a wider area. The churches enjoying a national remit, have attempted to step into that breach. St Enoch's, the first drugs project in Scotland, was associated through the local Franciscan Friary with the Catholic Church. This enabled it to acquire a disused seminary at Kilmanew House in Cardross (near Dumbarton) for a residential rehabilitation unit which had at one time housed up to seventy drug users. Later it was transferred to smaller premises in Wilton Street Maryhill (Glasgow), before being relocated in Red Tower, Helensburgh. The Church of Scotland had already had residential experience in the alcohol field. These units had begun to take in drug users also, when Britoil was successfully approached to fund a specific drug residential unit in Glasgow (Rainbow). Not to be outdone, the Episcopal Church gave over its rectory in Possilpark at the height of the 'heroin epidemic' in the area as a short-stay detox facility, a service which it has since continued to provide completely with the help of unpaid volunteers. Some other religious groups outside the mainstream churches have been active in trying to get drug users 'off the streets' although, as far as is known, only one such rehabilitation agency exists in Scotland (at Catrine in Ayrshire). Scotland's only private alcohol problems clinic (Castle Craig) has also taken drug users. In 1989, the Aberlour Trust opened accommodation in housing estates both in Edinburgh (Craigmillar) and Glasgow (Castlemilk) for women with alcohol and drug problems accompanied by their children. Phoenix House is a 'concept-oriented' residential care facility. This organization has six rehabilitation houses in England and has been in protracted discussion to open one in Glasgow.

It is difficult to say how all these voluntary projects would have survived simply as drug services. Most of them regarded their funding as provisional and usually on a year-to-year basis. The arrival of HIV infection changed all that. A long-established feature of the Scottish drug scene was the preference for injecting. This persisted even when the only available drugs were pharmaceutical products which had to be ground down or heated to become injectable. Scottish HIV infection figures are, as noted in Chapter 4, dramatically different from those in England. In 1991, over fifty per cent of recorded HIV infection in Scotland was among drug users. In addition, more than twenty-five per cent of such cases were female. The equivalent figures in England are eight per cent and seven per cent (Scottish Office Home and Health Department 1991). This indicated that there would have to be a significant stepping-up of drug services. In 1988, the original allocation of Government money for drug services was roughly doubled. Even more significantly, the decision was taken mainly to reinforce the projects already in place rather than search around for new ones. This meant that not only has the shape of a community-based service remained, but that also the contribution of the non-statutory sector has been strengthened. Nevertheless, HIV has remedicalised drug problems to a degree. The Advisory Council on the Misuse of Drugs (1988) expressed the view that HIV is a bigger problem than illicit drug use. This opinion is widely accepted among the workers in the drug problems field. A major concern therefore has been to get drug users into prescribing services to foster control of their drug use and in order to keep them out of custody and to reduce harm. Although most community projects would adhere to a harm-reduction model, few have prescribing facilities, but they are becoming used to dealing with detoxification programmes.

Since the advent of AIDS, a number of voluntary agencies have been developed by the gay community. These have offered support for drug users. It still remains to be seen whether such bodies have a sufficiently broad approach or appeal to attract young heterosexual drug users. Scottish AIDS Monitor and other groups are currently offering help. Milestone Hospice in Edinburgh is also open to drug users who require inpatient treatment. There have also been a number of initiatives by individuals in certain Scottish prisons. This is elaborated in Chapter 20.

It would appear, therefore, that the efforts of voluntary and community groups to gain credibility in the drugs field in the last decade have not been sufficiently sustained to respond adequately so far to drug problems compounded by the threat of HIV infection. After the first round of funding in the mid-1980s the projects gathered together in Stirling for a 'Drugs Fair'. Out of that came the Scottish Drugs Forum, whose management was deliberately balanced between the statutory and voluntary sectors. However, the statutory sector may be reluctant to see the even larger sums of money allocated for HIV going to the independent sector. One example is the failure to establish a 'Crisis Intervention Centre' which has long been regarded as necessary by drug workers. Of course, given the fact that such a provision does not exist in the alcohol field and would be extremely costly in the drugs field, the authorities may be employing a delaying tactic. The illegality of drugs such as heroin creates difficulties with the statutory sector that may appear inseparable without some kind of 'broker'. Even for that reason alone, the voluntary sector will be required to play an important role in the further development of drug services.

REFERENCES

Advisory Council on the Misuse of Drugs (1982) *Treatment and Rehabilitation*, London, Department of Health and Social Security, HMSO.
Advisory Council on the Misuse of Drugs (1988) *AIDS and Drug Misuse*, Part 1, London, HMSO.
ANSWER (1990) *AIDS News Supplement Weekly Report*, Glasgow, Communicable Diseases (Scotland) Unit, Ruchill Hospital, CD590 31–52.
Home Office (1980–90) *Statistics of the Misuse of Drugs in the United Kingdom*, London, Home Office.
Plant, M.A. and Plant, M.L. (1992) *Risk-Takers: Alcohol, Drugs, Sex and Youth*, London, Tavistock/Routledge.
Scottish Office Home and Health Department (1991) Press Release, August.

16. Services for problem drinkers in Scotland

BRUCE RITSON

INTRODUCTION

One of the earliest theses on the nature and treatment of alcohol dependence was submitted by Dr Thomas Trotter for an MD at Edinburgh University in 1778. Although he did not explicitly arrive at a concept of 'addiction', he did draw a parallel between alcohol and opium dependence. He described the abstinence syndrome, and the treatment his patients required, emphasising techniques that remain relevant to the present. He stressed the need to 'scrutinise the character of his patient, his pursuits, his modes of living, his very passions and private affairs' (Trotter 1804).

Such medical interest in alcohol misuse was not typical of the time. Throughout most of the nineteenth century, the predominant responses were in moral or legal terms. Nonetheless, a sizeable percentage of patients admitted to psychiatric hospitals during the nineteenth century were diagnosed as suffering from ailments related to alcohol misuse. The Inebriates (Scotland) Act (1898) empowered local authorities to establish reformatories for chronic inebriates, but these quickly fell into disuse because of the burden which such provisions placed on local rates. A similar reluctance to provide services for habitual drunken offenders was still evident in the 1980s.

The Temperance Movement, its political and social supporters and its detractors were probably the main voices in debate around the misuse of alcohol at the start of this century. This debate tended to centre on issues of availability, licensing hours and social reform rather than treatment and rehabilitation.

In 1947, Alcoholics Anonymous (AA) came to Scotland, and groups began to be established throughout the country. Apart from a few enthusiasts, there was relatively little medical interest in or acknowledgement of alcohol problems at that time. In 1952, the World Health Organization expert committee on mental health provided some stimulus in a report on alcoholism, which contained the following definition:

> Alcoholics are those excessive drinkers whose dependence on alcohol has attained such a degree that they show noticeable mental disturbance or interference with their mental and bodily health, their interpersonal relations and their smooth economic and social functioning or show prodromal signs of such developments. They therefore require treatment. (World Health Organization 1952).

It was unusual for a definition to contain a prescription, but it had some impact. In 1962, the Ministry of Health for England and Wales issued a memorandum to hospital authorities recommending the establishment of special 'units for the treatment of alcoholism' in each of the Regional Hospital Board areas. Scotland recognised similar needs, and one of the first of these new units was introduced by Professor Henry Walton in Edinburgh in 1963 (Walton et al. 1966; Scottish Home and Health Department 1965). The aims of this unit were to provide a service for the treatment of alcoholics along with training and research. Several units of this kind were established in Scotland during the following years. At first, most emphasised inpatient treatment of four to six weeks' duration, followed by outpatient attendance. Although located within the National Health Service, most established close links with social work and voluntary agencies such as AA and later Councils on Alcohol. Financed by the Health Service, they were usually staffed by psychiatrists, psychologists, social workers and nurses.

Throughout the 1970s increasing doubt was cast on the need for prolonged inpatient treatment for the majority of problem drinkers. Studies such as those by Edwards and Guthrie (1966) in England and Ritson (1967) and Chick et al. (1988) in Scotland, showed that simpler treatments, and particularly outpatient treatments, were often very effective, without the need for prolonged admissions.

This changing view of services for problem drinkers culminated in the report of the Advisory Committee on Alcoholism (1978) entitled 'Pattern and range of services from problem drinkers'. This concluded that the services should be aimed at 'any person who experiences social, psychological or physical problems as a consequence of his or her own repeated drinking of alcohol or the repeated drinking of others'. Treatment, when possible, should be provided at the primary level.

The main tasks at this primary level were to recognise problem drinking, have an adequate knowledge of the help required by the problem drinker and the family, give this help as far as practicable and know when and where to seek expert help and provide continuing care and support before, during and after any period of specialist treatment. The main tasks of the services at the secondary level were to provide specialised knowledge, advice and support for those who needed it at primary level. This structure has become the foundation of the organization of services in Scotland. It is elaborated in Table 16.1.

Level 1	Drinker; family, friends
Level 2	Social Security, publicans, police, employer
Level 3	Primary health care team, social work, general hospital casualty department, clergy, counselling agencies
Level 4	Specialist social work services, AA, AlAnon, Councils on Alcohol, NHS Units

Table 16.1. Levels of intervention with harmful drinking

In this model, the individual drinker has primary responsibility for taking care of his or her own drinking. It is towards the individual drinker that health promotion is directed. At this level, family and friends of the drinker embody the normative influences which at one point may encourage drinking, at another criticise and impose sanctions. It is clear that many problem drinkers change their habits in response to these informal influences without recourse to any 'treatment agency' (Saunders and Kershaw 1979).

At the next level are services with no designated responsibility for treating or counselling problem drinkers. Nonetheless, they commonly encounter problem drinkers at times of crisis. The police, lawyers and the courts have all noted that problems related to drinking take up a great deal of their time (Ritson 1985). Hamilton et al. (1978) showed that it was feasible and desirable to divert habitual drunken offenders from the courts and to provide detoxification facilities, but these also required adequate follow-up and rehabilitation. In Aberdeen, Albyn House showed the powerful effect which a service of this kind could have on the number of drunken offenders coming through the courts. This is described further in Chapter 18. It is surprising that, like earlier attempts, little support has been found to create detoxification and rehabilitation facilities for drunken offenders.

Alcohol and employment policies have become widespread in Scotland principally as a result of the stimulus provided by the Scottish Council on Alcohol. This has been described in Chapter 15. Alcohol and Employment Policies or Employee Assistance Programmes facilitate the early detection of alcohol problems and provide an incentive for change before the worker's performance has been seriously impaired (Hore and Plant 1981; Plant 1984).

At the third level are agencies which are commonly the first point of contact for problem drinkers at a time of crisis, a crisis which may not necessarily have an alcohol problem as its principal focus. The presenting concern may be rent arrears, housing problems, marital discord, a fractured femur, an upset stomach, depression or anxiety on the part of the drinker's spouse and children. The range is enormous. Therefore the family doctor, Accident and Emergency departments, general hospital outpatient departments, social workers and counselling agencies all have a crucial role in the early recognition of alcohol problems and in providing adequate front-line help. The benefits and feasibility of both recognition and early intervention are clear. Projects such as DRAMS promoted by the Health Education Board for Scotland (HEBS) (1991) for general practitioners and the report by Chick et al. (1985) in general medical wards have shown that simple intervention given to problem drinkers identified early can produce significant health benefits. Social workers have also developed guidelines on early recognition and intervention (Social Work Services Group 1986).

If primary level services are to work effectively in this way, they need regular support from the specialist agencies outlined in level four. One way of linking the specialist services with those in the front line is the creation of Community Alcohol Teams. These teams commonly include a community psychiatric nurse, a psychologist, a social worker, counsellors and a psychiatrist. A small number of such teams have been established in Scotland. Although their benefits have never been clearly demonstrated, they nonetheless seem to be a sensible basis for multidisciplinary working in the community (Stockwell and Clements 1987).

Specialist treatment services within the National Health Service continue to be based in most cases on hospitals with outreach in the community. Community psychiatric nurses have proved effective in providing both links with front-line agencies and in supervising detoxification of patients in their own homes.

Specialised treatment in hospital has been modified considerably over the past twenty years. There is an increasing emphasis on outpatient treatment, and the length of stay has commonly shrunk to an average of one or two weeks. Much longer inpatient stays are still commonplace in the private sector, of which a few examples exist in Scotland.

Trends in the organization of specialist services seem likely to be towards a much more varied menu of treatment options. All services now place an emphasis on the importance of seeking help at an early stage before serious damage to health and psychological and social welfare has occurred. The studies of matching client needs to specific therapies are an important direction for future research.

Drug treatments have had a modest part in the treatment of alcohol problems. Antabuse (Disulfiram) is quite commonly used by some centres. There are also studies of the efficacy of medicines which reduce craving or demand for alcohol, but these are in a very early stage of development. This is discussed further in Chapter 21.

GROUPS WITH SPECIAL NEEDS.

The majority of problem drinkers are served by primary level agencies supported by specialist services from the voluntary, health and social work sectors. However, there remain some clients who are liable to slip through this net if their needs are not specifically addressed. These include:

Homeless problem drinkers

In each city in Scotland, there are a sizeable number of men and a smaller number of women who have serious alcohol problems and are also homeless. A number of these also find themselves in the category of habitual drunken offenders, often because their drunkenness is highly visible and leads to police intervention.

Rehabilitation hostels for this group are commonly 'dry' and provide a residential community in which individuals can remain abstinent while they concentrate on coming to terms with making changes in their style of life. Some are provided by Social Work Departments such as Thornybauk in Edinburgh, while others have been the responsibility of the voluntary sector, such as the Church of Scotland and the Salvation Army. In some areas, day facilities are available where the individual can socialise in a drink-free environment.

Young people

Alcohol dependence is relatively uncommon among young people, but alcohol misuse is very common indeed. Intoxication among young men is commonly related to crime and various accidents on the road and at work. In Dundee, a programme for the retraining of young offenders who have drinking problems showed that considerable benefits followed when they were referred to a series of seminars concerning sensible drinking and avoiding offending. Many courts now have a court social worker particularly concerned with delinquency of this kind who makes a link with an appropriate educational programme, often as part of a probation order (see Chapter 13).

Rehabilitation services for drink offenders have not yet been developed in Scotland, though there have been promises that they will be instituted in the near future. Focus initially seems likely to be on those who are seen as high-risk offenders.

Women

It is commonly felt that women find it harder to seek help with alcohol problems either because they feel the stigma more acutely and this acts as a deterrent or because the services arranged do not meet their particular needs. Many clinics now provide women-only groups, and voluntary services have established some special services uniquely for women such as the LIBRA Group in Edinburgh.

Other special needs

Ethnic minorities often find it difficult to reach appropriate services, and the needs of these groups in Scotland are only gradually being acknowledged. The elderly are often overlooked and have special needs, as do homosexuals who have alcohol-related problems.

CONCLUSIONS

Those who suffer from alcohol problems come from all walks of life, social classes and occupations. It should be clear that alcohol problems are not homogenous but present an enormous range both in degree of severity and in their presenting characteristics. The pattern of services in Scotland must be sufficiently adaptable to cater for individuals in urban centres as well as rural communities that are among the most remote in Europe. No single pattern of service can suit such diversity. The aim should be to provide a comprehensive and well-coordinated network of support that will meet the needs of both the individual and their families. Several attempts have been made to ensure that such a network exists. Nonetheless, it is clear that the availability of services remains patchy. In 1985, the Scottish Health Education Coordinating Committee (the Crofton Committee) outlined a blueprint for the prevention of alcohol problems. Its recommendations were unambiguous, but only part of the task which it set out has been accomplished. More recently, the Scottish Office Home and Health Department has encouraged the development of regional alcohol coordinating groups which will plan an integral service. The Scottish Council on Alcohol (1989) has pointed to the importance of working together to minimise the extent of alcohol problems in each community. It will be a pity if preventive services are seen as being separate from those concerned with treatment, because the techniques which they share, such as the information used in DRAMS or drinking sensibly, are often interchangeable.

Although alcohol is undoubtedly 'our favourite drug' in Scotland, it would be short-sighted to see alcohol services working in isolation from those concerned with other forms of substance misuse (Royal College of Psychiatrists 1986). The techniques involved are similar, and often the client group shows considerable overlap. A sizeable percentage of alcohol misusers report a history of drug misuse, and this is particularly true of Benzodiazepine abuse. There is a growing tendency for services to be combined either in their entirety or at least in the sphere of organization and planning.

REFERENCES

Advisory Committee on Alcoholism (1978) *Pattern and Range of Services for Problem Drinkers*, London, HMSO

Chick, J., Lloyd, G. and Crombie, E. (1985) 'Counselling problem drinkers in medical wards: a controlled study'. *British Medical Journal* 290 965–7.

Chick, J., Ritson, E.B., Connaughton, B., Stewart, A. and Chick, J. (1988) 'Extended treatment for alcoholism – a controlled study', *British Journal of Addiction* 83, 625–34.

Edwards, G. and Guthrie, S. (1967) 'A controlled trial of inpatient and outpatient treatment of alcohol dependence', *Lancet* 1, 555–9.

Hamilton, J.R., Griffith, A., Ritson, B. and Aitken, C. (1978) *Detoxification of Habitual Drunken Offenders*, Study no. 39, Scottish Home and Health Department, Edinburgh.

Health Education Board for Scotland (1991) *DRAMS (Drinking Responsibly and Moderately with Self-Control*, Edinburgh, HEBS.

Hore, B. and Plant, M.A. (eds) (1981) *Alcohol Problems in Employment*, London, Croom Helm.

Ministry of Health (1962) *Hospital Treatment of Alcoholism*, Memorandum HM (62), London, Ministry of Health.

Plant, M.A. (1984) 'Alcohol problems in employment: The emerging response'. *European Management Journal* 2, 34–40.

Ritson, E.B. (1968) 'The prognosis of alcohol addicts treated by a specialist unit', *British Journal of Psychiatry* 114, p. 1019.

Ritson, E.B. (1985) *Community Response to Alcohol-Related Problems*, Geneva, World Health Organization.

Royal College of Psychiatrists (1986) *Alcohol: Our Favourite Drug*, London, Tavistock.

Saunders, W.M. and Kershaw, P.W. (1979) 'Spontaneous remission from alcoholism – a community study', *British Journal of Addiction* 74, 251–65.

Scottish Council on Alcohol (1989) *A National Strategy on Alcohol*, Glasgow, Scottish Council on Alcohol.

Scottish Health Education Coordinating Committee (1985) *Health Education in the Prevention of Alcohol-Related Problems* (Crofton report), Edinburgh, Scottish Health Education Coordinating Committee.

Scottish Home and Health Department (1965) *Alcoholism: Report on Health Services for Treatment and Rehabilitation*, Edinburgh, HMSO.

Social Work Services Group (1988) *Towards Effective Practice with Problem Drinkers*, Edinburgh, HMSO.

Stockwell, T. and Clement, S. (eds) (1987) *Helping the Problem Drinker*, London, Croom Helm.

Trotter, T. (1804) *An Essay Medical, Philosophical and Chemical on Drunkenness and its Effects on the Human Body*, London, Longman.

Walton, H.J., Ritson, E.B. and Kennedy, R.I. (1966) 'Response of alcoholics to clinic treatment', *British Medical Journal* 2, 1171.

World Health Organization (1952) *Expert Committee on Mental Health, Alcohol Subcommittee Tech. Rep. Ser.*, No 48, Geneva, World Health Organization.

17. Services for problem drug users in Scotland

JUDY GREENWOOD

HISTORICAL PERSPECTIVE

In the late seventies in Britain, an epidemic of drug-taking (mainly heroin) occurred, especially in the deprived inner-city areas and council housing estates (MacGregor 1989; Berridge 1990; Plant and Plant 1992). Scotland was no exception to this trend.

In some areas the route of administration was governed by the availability of the drug, plentiful supplies leading to oral intake or inhaling ('chasing the dragon') and poor supplies leading to injecting. In other areas, the local culture seemed to dictate the prevalence of injecting regardless of availability. If injecting was the norm, as it was in Edinburgh, the prevalence of needle-sharing would depend on the availability of injecting equipment (Strang and Stimson 1990).

By 1984, a main surgical supplier in Edinburgh had ceased operating, which led to an acute shortage in injecting equipment. This coincided with increased activity from the local police drug squad and courts. The latter began imposing heavy sentences on anyone caught in possession of even small amounts of heroin. Probably as a result, drug users began injecting their drugs on the dealer's premises to avoid arrest, often in the company of fellow injectors and sharing the injecting equipment. At around the same time, silently and unbeknown to drug users, doctors, the legal system, and police, the HIV virus also arrived in south-east Scotland. This is elaborated in Chapter 6. Within a few years, up to fifty per cent of drug users who had been injecting in Edinburgh and Dundee between 1983 and 1885 were found to be HIV-infected (Roberston et al. 1986).

Remarkably, the HIV epidemic has not spread extensively among drug users in the west of Scotland, despite the fact that drug users in Strathclyde are now almost twice as likely to inject as drug users from the south-east.

DEVELOPMENT OF DRUG SERVICES

About the same time that the HIV virus became established in Scotland, Scottish psychiatrists and the Scottish Office agreed that the main support services for the new wave of drug users should be community-based non-statutory drug agencies. This involved a shift in focus away from specialist drug-dependency units which, in the past, had not been particularly effective. Additional funding was provided to establish a network of local non-statutory drug agencies in areas known to have a high incidence of drug use. These agencies offered counselling and family support and in some cases, operated drop-in day centres. Most specialist residential accommodation for drug-dependency problems was also non-statutory, with the exception of one specialist inpatient drug agency in Glasgow. General psychiatrists would see drug users in general clinics and, if thought appropriate and relevant, admit them to acute psychiatric wards. Some general practitioners developed a special interest in and expertise in relation to drug problems from their contact with drug users. In a few areas in Scotland, social services also established community-based drug workers.

Once the full significance of the Scottish HIV epidemic virus became apparent in 1986, infectious disease consultants and virologists became a key interface between the medical profession and drug users. Some enlightened consultants began prescribing methadone to HIV-positive drug users in a bid to maintain their health and to ensure that they returned regularly to the hospital for follow-up. Soon, HIV-negative drug users also demanded methadone substitution therapy, but health boards stipulated that only infected patients should be treated by infectious disease staff.

INJECTING EQUIPMENT EXCHANGE SCHEMES

In 1987, the central government set up experimental initiatives in three Scottish cities, Glasgow, Edinburgh and Dundee. As noted in Chapter 6, the third lasted for only a few weeks because of serious threats to staff by drug users who disliked its regulations. The Glasgow clinic was picketed for several months by angry members of the general public. Paradoxically, four years later, eight needle exchanges now flourish in that city and provide the main thrust of drug services with little change in the abstinence model and 'rejection of prescribing' advocated by Glasgow's psychiatrists.

Perhaps as a result, ninety-one per cent of registered drug users in Strathclyde continue to inject regularly. Surprisingly, in a city only seventy kilometres away from Edinburgh, the HIV infection rate amongst its drug users has remained remarkably low, with fewer than five per cent thought to be infected. Nevertheless, considerable concern exists about the potential dangers of HIV in Glasgow, and, as a result, excellent community-based services for pregnant drug users and a neighbourhood drop-in centre for prostitutes, many of whom are drug users, have been established. These offer a wide range of harm-reduction and support services, backed up by some family doctors and community drug teams.

Edinburgh's Community Drug Problem Service (CDPS)

The experiences gained by the author and Dr George Bath from running the needle exchange in Leith (Edinburgh) for a year led to the establishment of a Community Drug Problem Service (CDPS) in 1988. The CDPS is financed by the Lothian Health Board's AIDS budget. At the same time, the injecting equipment exchange scheme was expanded to cover a wider area (Greenwood 1990).

Because of the high prevalence of HIV infection in Edinburgh, the main aims of the CDPS were to provide a harm-reduction service for those not ready to cease drug-taking and a drug treatment service for those motivated to stop. The target population was young intravenous drug users, whose average age was twenty-five and of whom two thirds were male and one third female. During 1988, such individuals were injecting mainly buprenorphine (Temgesic) and temazepam (Normison), as street heroin had become scarce due to a successful campaign by the local Drug Squad aimed at drug dealers. If injectable drugs were unavailable, most drug users would use dihydrocodeine and/or diazepam. Polydrug use was commonplace. The majority had rarely worked, and lived in deprived housing schemes characterised by high unemployment. Many also reported parental separation and other stressful life events. Of those tested for HIV, thirty per cent were seropositive.

The CDPS is based at the Royal Edinburgh Hospital, but staff work with drug users in community health centres or in their own homes. The staff share their care with existing non-statutory drug agencies and local general practitioners (GPs) who are asked to undertake prescribing when appropriate. In this respect, the service differs from drug services which contemporaneously developed in Dundee, Dumfries and Ayr with similar aims but relying more extensively on centralised prescribing.

The hierarchy of objectives for the services are:
- to make contact with as many drug users as possible
- to stop needle and syringe sharing and unsafe sex
- to stabilise drug intake and lifestyle
- to reduce criminal behaviour and imprisonment
- to reduce drug intake
- to encourage abstinence from drugs.

At the CDPS, after assessment, a multidisciplinary team meeting outlines a provisional management strategy subject to the GP's agreement to prescribe. The latter usually involves the daily dispensing by a pharmacist of oral drugs in a stable or decreasing dosage, depending on the drug user's current motivation to withdraw from drugs. An agreement is also signed by the drug users, in which they agree to see a key worker from the CDPS for counselling and support on a regular basis. They also agree to negotiate with the key worker rather than the GP for any change in prescription, to give random urine samples and to avoid continued chaotic street drug use, especially by injection, while on the prescribed regime.

Initially, GPs were encouraged to share in the care of Edinburgh's estimated 3000 to 4000 intravenous drug users by an explanatory letter. This was reinforced by a series of evening meetings to highlight the dangers of HIV among drug injectors in the city, regular case conferences at GP surgeries, and a series of articles on drugs and HIV issues mailed to every Lothian GP.

Later, the CDPS sectorised its service so that, in each quadrant, a community psychiatric nurse (CPN) and clinical assistant would develop a closer relationship with a limited group of GPs and local drug and social workers. It also introduced a clinic at which the first three days of methadone are given on site in order to observe the clinical effect and to titrate the optimal dose for each patient. Then three weeks of clinic prescribing are offered before the drug user is handed back to the GP. The latter would have agreed to the handover before the programme was started. Physical health checks and HIV testing are also offered by the clinical assistants. The team has the services of a consultant psychiatrist, a psychologist and a social worker as well as Community Psychiatric Nurses.

EFFECTS OF THE HARM-REDUCTION APPROACH

In Dundee and Edinburgh, there has been a high referral rate. Over a third of Edinburgh's estimated intravenous drug users have been referred, with a sixty-five per cent attendance rate, suggesting that both GPs (the main referring agents) and drug users are satisfied with the service offered. Half of patients seen each year are carried over into the subsequent year. The prolonged contact is seen as essential to promote real changes in the drug users' lifestyles and maturation.

Injecting rates, according to Home Office notifications, have dropped dramatically in cities with a liberal prescribing policy: fifty-five per cent in Dundee, sixty-one per cent in Edinburgh compared to ninety-one per cent in Glasgow and ninety-six per cent in the Forth Valley. Such statistics are confirmed by the Scottish Drug Misuse Database Statistics (Scottish Health Service 1992) and by clinical observation of those continuing in treatment and by prison medical officers' observations of newly admitted prisoners in Lothian, who now rarely show signs of injecting whereas on whom, three years ago, track marks were rife. This is discussed further in Chapter 20.

Drug users who remain in treatment provisionally appear to stay out of prison longer and are more likely to be working. The incidence of HIV infection among new referrals has dropped from thirty-seven per cent in 1988 to eleven per cent in 1990. Such changes, which precede treatment, can be attributed to a combination of factors: good health education campaigns, availability of clean injecting equipment, 'street wisdom' or personal knowledge of other drug users with HIV or AIDS and the increased availability of non-injectable drugs. Approximately half of CDPS patients are on a reducing prescription, with many stabilised on low doses and a few now leading drug-free lives.

The predicted advantages of GP prescribing in Edinburgh have been confirmed after three years of experience. A shared-care approach means that more patients can be offered harm-reduction and more GPs are encouraged to work with, and learn about, drug users. In addition, more drug users are offered regular health care, which is relevant to those who have not been tested as HIV seropositive. Drug users are treated as 'normal' patients and GPs have often known them since childhood, a perspective which helps in the shared decision-making and shared-care approach.

CONCLUSIONS

Scottish drug services represent a mosaic of approaches and responses to the current wave of drug-taking in socially-deprived young people. In some regions, the emphasis has been on punishment and control, with little evidence of specialised drug services, especially in rural areas. In other areas, such as Strathclyde, the emphasis has been on harm-reduction through injecting equipment exchanges, with less stress on the dangers of injecting. In Edinburgh and Dundee, however, the high prevalence of HIV infection has brought into sharp focus the need for a broad range of harm-reduction strategies. Liberal substitute prescribing policies have evolved which appear to have dramatically reduced the incidence of injecting among local drug users.

The cooperation of Edinburgh's GPs has been exemplary and impressive, as they have played a crucial role in the shared care of drug users. Whether such liberal policies will lead to drug users becoming bored with the predictability of prescribed drugs or stopping using them, or whether a new form of dealing will develop with increased street leakage of the prescribed drugs to new recruits into the drug scene, is unknown. Many powerful forces foster drug misuse. These include unemployment, family breakdown and peer-group pressure, and the chronic state of hopelessness and low self-esteem (Fazey 1977). Against such pressures, the combined forces of increased customs control, police and prison activity, injecting equipment exchanges, drug services, health education and social services can do little to stem the rising tide of drug-taking in some communities. But, perhaps much can be done to alter professional and public attitudes towards drug-takers, by offering them at least the dignity to take their drugs more safely without the dangers of HIV infection. HIV/AIDS risks amongst drug users, as noted by Stimson et al. (1988), Strang and Stimson (1990), can be reduced, even if they may not realistically be eradicated. It is likely that illicit drug dependence will persist so long as sections of the community are subject to multiple deprivation and social disadvantage.

REFERENCES

Berridge, V. (Ed.), (1990) *Drug Research and Policy in Britain*, Aldershot, Avebury.

Fazey, C. (1977) *The ætiology of Psychoactive Drug Use*, Paris, UNESCO.

Greenwood, J. (1990) 'Creating a new drug service in Edinburgh', *British Medical Journal* 300, 587–9.

MacGregor, S. (Ed.), (1989) *Drugs and British Society*, London, Tavistock/Routledge.

Plant, M.A. and Plant, M.L. (1992) *Risk-Takers: Alcohol, Drugs, Sex and Youth*, London, Tavistock/Routledge.

Robertson, J.R., Bucknall, A.B.V., Welsby, P.D. et al. (1986) 'Epidemic of AIDS-related virus infection amongst intravenous drug abusers', *British Medical Journal* 292, 527–9.

Scottish Health Service (1992) *Scottish Drug Misuse Database October 1990 – March 1991*, Edinburgh, Common Services Agency, ISD Publications.

Stimson, G.V., Aldritt, L., Dolan, K., Donaghue, M. and Lart, R.A. (1988) *Injecting Equipment Exchange Schemes / Final Report*, Monitoring Research Group, Goldsmiths College, University of London.

Strang, J. and Stimson, G.V. (Eds) (1990) *AIDS and Drug Misuse*, London, Tavistock/Routledge.

18. Social work services for problem drinkers and drug users

MARY HARTNOLL*

Concern with the personal and social effects of alcohol misuse has been associated with social work from its beginning. The roots of the probation service, now part of Scottish social work departments, lie in the work of philanthropic agencies which convinced courts that they could rehabilitate offenders whose behaviour originated from drunkenness. Magistrates could choose to discharge offenders with a condition of good behaviour to the care and supervision of 'missionaries' appointed by temperance or voluntary agencies.

The link between the misuse of alcohol or illicit drugs and offending behaviour is again receiving prominence through the introduction in 1991 of new national standards for social work with offenders. These highlight the importance of assessing the role of substance abuse in offending behaviour and making recommendations to the court about possible disposals.

At the same time, the provisions of the National Health Service and Community Care Act (1990) include specific social work responsibility for services in the community for people who abuse alcohol or drugs. One of the main objectives of this development is a coordinated range of services to meet the need identified.

These measures come at a time when currents have been running towards a social care model of response to substance abuse rather than relying mainly on a medical treatment response. This can include a number of strategies – from a minimal intervention model of providing advice and information through counselling directed at individual behaviour to more formal day or residential programmes. The running in this process has not only been made within social work itself. In 1987,

*   Collated with contributions from Strathclyde Social Work Department, Albyn House Association and other voluntary and statutory social work agencies in Scotland.

the Chief Social Work Adviser at the Scottish Office was able to state: 'many social work practitioners remain ... uncertain about how to help clients to change their drinking behaviour' (Scottish Office 1987). Much the same could be said in the context of drug use. Social Work Departments have been addressing issues relating to the organization of services and the training implications, but it is recognised that the necessary developments in capabilities and confidence have some way to go.

A number of factors contribute to this. The disease concept of 'alcoholism' underpins the philosophy and methods of many major contributors to the service provision, such as Alcoholics Anonymous, which undoubtedly brings benefit to many. Although its limitations have been recognised (Shaw et al. 1978; Shaw 1982), the emphasis on treatment remains a potent force in service provision. Social workers who accept uncritically the concept of illness underestimate their own skills and deny clients access to a different approach which might have more relevance to them.

A second factor which has contributed to the uncertainty about the social work role is unfamiliarity with developing ideas and new techniques. Saunders (1985) has highlighted some of the difficulties for social work:

- late involvement with problem alcohol or drug users which mean intractable social problems have built up
- lack of awareness of the potential effectiveness of early counselling
- perceived pessimism in developing and sustaining motivation for change.

Responses to these challenges include training in specific techniques such as motivational interviewing and methods for anticipating and dealing with relapse. There is also a need for increased opportunities for intervention at the optimum stage of development of problem drinking and the establishment of supportive specialist resources.

A third factor is the difficulty of rethinking the varying components of effective intervention and allocating responsibilities to best effect. Pursuing a social care model does not deny the essential role of health care services. The stage of detoxification and the management of withdrawal may sometimes require specific medical treatment. The lifestyles of problem alcohol and drug users can be accompanied with self-neglect or associated infections or injuries. For some, substance misuse is accompanied by mental ill health which requires specialist medical help. Equally, skills in counselling, advising or supporting are well represented in primary health care staff. The role of social work within the context of a social care – and community-based approach is to match need with the coordination of planned programmes of care and treatment to ensure that all the appropriate elements of service are identified.

Finally, there is a hesitancy among social workers to have confidence in their own competence. The skills of assessment, offering information and advice, counselling and coordinating multiple involvement are a regular part of social work practice. Yet the presence of alcohol or drug-related factors can cause confusion and apprehension, resulting in an instinctive response to refer the case on to another agency. It is important not to allow the sense of mystique which too easily attaches to working with alcohol and drug problems to undermine social workers' confidence in their own ability. Basic skills can be enhanced by precise knowledge about substance misuse and specific techniques. The joy of many minimal intervention techniques is that they can show effective outcomes from comparatively little input and can draw on the client's own resources of self-help. Even where more intensive work is required, unless the alcohol and drug-related factors are taken into account, little progress will be made.

These factors could, if not countered, impede the social policy impetus to place responsibility for rehabilitative services for alcohol and drug problems with social work departments and voluntary agencies in the social care field. Ownership of this social hot potato has passed from the Temperance Movement and the churches to medical specialists and is now moving to counsellors and social workers. As Saunders (1985) shows, at the very least, they can do no worse than their predecessors in terms of measured outcome. The best outcome from effective community care policies would be the integration of the varying professional inputs with the needs and strengths of the client and the resources in the community. This topic is discussed further in Chapter 22.

Although these factors have slowed the development of services towards a social care model, there have been many advances in Scotland in the development of social work services with both alcohol and drug abusers. The following are examples of the opportunities presented within ordinary social work practice.

EARLY INTERVENTION

Many studies have demonstrated that before substance abuse problems are recognised, individuals are well established in a pattern of regular excessive use (e.g. Thorley 1985). This can lead to an erosion of factors such as social stability and personal support which would otherwise assist rehabilitation (Costello 1980). Although individuals will rarely approach Social Work Departments directly in relation to alcohol or drug-related problems, many seek help and advice over financial or family concerns or are referred by other agencies for other reasons. Social workers are well placed to offer an effective screening service in relation to incipient alcohol or drug problems.

CHILDREN AND YOUNG PEOPLE

Social workers have particular responsibilities in respect of children and young people whose life circumstances make them particularly vulnerable to drug or alcohol misuse. Some will be in care and/or under statutory supervision in their own homes. Others will be members of families referred for a variety of family or social problems. In working both directly with young people and with families where substance misuse is a factor, the importance of supportive relationships in stimulating motivation and establishing and sustaining freedom from addiction is an essential part of social work practice. The process of addressing the problems associated with substance misuse may be more constructive than focusing on the substance itself.

SOCIAL WORK IN THE CRIMINAL JUSTICE SERVICE

Social work in the context of offending behaviour often offers an opportunity for intervention at the point of crisis. This can provide the motivation for change which is needed, and the legal sanctions implicit in statutory orders may be helpful in securing progress. Conditions may be attached to probation orders, parole or Community Service Orders which require attendance for counselling or for a programme at a day centre or for a period of residential care. The essential factor is to target intervention on those aspects of behaviour which can be modified. There is evidence that too much reliance on rigid conditions can obscure areas of real personal progress. A balance has to be achieved which offers structured assistance and maintains the commitment of the offender to tackle his or her behaviour.

The emphasis so far in this chapter has been on direct social work intervention. Reference has been made to the community care legislation in the field of alcohol and drug misuse. An essential aspect of the legislation is its emphasis on local authorities working with agencies in the independent sector to develop specific services. One example of this approach which predated the legislation is Albyn House, Aberdeen. It is an innovative approach to a particular aspect of alcohol misuse

A DESCRIPTION

Albyn House is a charitable registered company set up to receive and care for persons arrested by the police as 'drunk and incapable'. It has a staffing level of sixteen full-time and two part-time workers.

There are four designated beds for 'drunk and incapable' referrals and fourteen beds in the care hostel. There is also a halfway house facility of four beds. The venture started operation in 1983 and has to date received over 6,000 'drunk and incapable' referrals, currently running at 850–900 per annum.

Its funding is heavily reliant on deficit funding from Grampian Region Social Work Department. It receives a small grant from Grampian Health Board and the remainder of its revenue funding comes from board and lodging charges for the care hostel.

THE WORK

As Robert Straus, the sociologist, observed, 'Alcohol as a substance is capable of permeating all the tissues of the human body and ... alcohol problems permeate virtually all the issues of human society' (Straus 1974). In his biographical study 'Escape from Custody' he charts the life course of a homeless alcohol dependent man and reinforces the theme he developed in 'Non-addictive pathology drinking studies of homeless men' that dependence on a substance is often more episodic in nature than a permanent behaviour (Straus 1974; Straus and McCarthy 1951). His initial quote encompasses the effect that alcohol may have in society as a whole, and his in-depth study of one man demonstrates in a very personal way the chaos which alcohol creates for an individual.

Albyn House is essentially a social response to one of the problems created by alcohol's ability to permeate all areas of society. Albyn House operates first and foremost as a designated centre for the diversion of persons arrested for public drunkenness from the criminal justice system. Another Designated Centre, Beechwood House, opened in Inverness in 1991. The concept is by no means new. In 1892, the offence of 'drunk and incapable' entered the statute book. However, even then, the issue of habitual drunkenness offenders needing help rather than punishment led to the Inebriates Act of 1898. Aberdeen housed one of the Inebriate Reformatories of that time.

REFERRALS

The persons who have been referred to Albyn House over the years have represented all demographic sections of society, with some fifty per cent of all those admitted having permanent addresses and social supports. The majority of these individuals have been referred once only, thereby largely avoiding the 'revolving door' syndrome as observed by Lloyd and Taylor (1986).

The care hostel has dealt with a more skewed population, with some ninety per cent of the 300 referrals to date being of no fixed abode on entry. Some fifty of these individuals have since been rehoused, the majority of whom are successfully maintaining their tenancies, some with aftercare provided by the support worker.

Others have been offered assistance with problems ranging from diet, shelter and care to in-depth assessment and rehabilitation, aimed at attaining a better quality of life and reducing the destructive episodes with which homeless drinkers are often associated.

DEFINITION OF EXTENT OF PROBLEMS

Shaw et al. (1985) identified three possible client groups: occasional drunkenness offenders; habitual drunkenness offenders; and other problem drinkers. The authors ascertained that the majority of drunkenness offences were committed by persons for whom drunkenness was the only offence, which is one of the reasons that Albyn House elected for designated status rather than the broader and less well-defined role of a detoxification centre.

The report further discovered that the extent of alcohol-related damage experienced by such referral types would be high. This has been detected in research carried out at Albyn House by Donnelly (1988), whose use of Severity of Alcohol Dependence Questionnaire (SADQ) scores identified that seventy-six per cent of the study group interviewed showed severe alcohol dependence. The mean score of 38.2 was higher than other comparative studies (e.g. Stockwell et al. 1983; Potamianos et al. 1984).

Shaw et al. (1985) established criteria which they judged to be necessary to provide an effective service:

- accessibility for potential clients
- treatment programme (diversity of provision)
- continuity of provision, working system of services and referral out
- specialism.

Albyn House has direct access for the drunkenness offender via Grampian Police. It also accepts general practitioner referrals to the care hostel. It offers treatment packages tailored to the individual and not tied to a particular philosophy on addiction. It operates good working relationships with the police and care agencies, and offers follow-up and after-care to both designated and hostel referrals.

DETACHED WORK

Albyn House is one example of a specialist resource which diverts people with alcohol problems from the criminal justice system and offers a more constructive approach. Detached work is another example of an alternative model of working which is being developed by social workers in statutory and voluntary agencies. Its main characteristics include making contact with drug users in locations such as pubs and clubs or on the streets and using the opportunity to offer information, informal counselling and access to appropriate helping agencies.

Drug users tend not to identify their use of drugs itself as a problem but only to seek help when the associated problems become overwhelming. They may be unwilling to refer themselves to agencies which they regard as having an authority role especially in respect of illicit activities. Parents of young children may be particularly anxious because they fear being deemed unfit to continue caring for their children. Detached work can be both a means of taking services to the drug users and of presenting a different and more acceptable aspect of the authority's services without in any way compromising its statutory responsibilities.

The Possilpark Drug Project is located in an area of high drug usage in Glasgow. It provides both a service to drug users who refer themselves and an outreach service through detached drug workers. It provides evidence of the potential for outreach work to target work on groups who are traditionally less disposed to use available services. The people seen by the detached drug workers are consistently in a younger age group than those who refer themselves for help. In 1989/90, sixty-eight per cent of the detached drug workers' clients were aged twenty-five or under and, of them, sixty-six per cent were under twenty years of age. This compared with sixty-four per cent of the self-referred. In 1990/91, forty-seven per cent of those in contact with a detached worker were between sixteen and twenty years old, compared with twenty-seven per cent of those who referred themselves.

Two other benefits of targeting can be seen. In 1990/91, twenty-four per cent of new clients coming to the project were female, while for the detached workers the figure was thirty-two per cent. In relation to harm-minimisation, all new contacts were asked whether they shared needles. Only twenty per cent of self-referrals in 1990/91 said they did, whereas the figure for the detached worker contacts was seventy-five per cent. The comparable figures for 1989/90 were thirty-nine and ninety-four per cent which indicates that a little progress has been made in highlighting the risks associated with needle-sharing, although much more needs to be done.

CONCLUSIONS

The work done by Social Work Departments and voluntary agencies in Scotland reflects the diversity of problems presented by alcohol and substance misuse. There are a number of interesting specific developments, but perhaps the most positive way forward can be found through building on the existing skills and knowledge of social workers across the whole spectrum of social work. Social workers do not work in isolation from other professional groups, and recognising the existence of an alcohol or drug problem may allow access to a different range of services. The changes in both community care and criminal justice legislation require local authorities to prepare a coordinated strategy which offers a community response to people who abuse alcohol or drugs. The emphasis on coordination and cooperation means that services should not be in competition with each other. Social work is one approach which is now making its own distinctive contribution to the huge range of human problems encompassed by the phrase 'alcohol and drug abuse'.

REFERENCES

Costello, R. (1980) 'Alcoholism treatment effectiveness', in Edwards, G. and Grant, M. *'Alcoholism Treatment in Transition'*, London, Croom Helm.

Donnelly, J.C. (1988) 'The role of Albyn House in the care and rehabilitation of drunkenness offenders and a description of the client population', Unpublished elective report, University of Aberdeen Medical School.

Heather, N. and Robertson, I. (1985) *Problem Drinking: The New Approach*, Harmondsworth, Pelican.

Lloyd, S. and Taylor, A. (1986) 'Public drunkenness and the role of a designated place', Department of Social Work, University of Aberdeen, King's College, p. 55.

Potamianous, G., Gorman, D.M., Duffy, S.W. and Peters, T.J. (1984) 'The use of the Severity of Alcohol Dependence Questionnaire (SADQ) on a sample of problem drinkers presenting at a district general hospital.', *Alcohol* 1, 441–5.

Saunders, W. (1985) 'Counselling problem drinkers: Research and practice. In: Lishman, J. (ed.) *Approaches to Addiction – Research Highlights in Social Work*, London, Kogan Page, II.

Scottish Office (1987) *Towards Effective Practice with Problem Drinkers*, Social Work Services Group Guidance, Edinburgh, HMSO.

Shaw, S. (1992) 'What is problem drinking?' in Plant, M.A. (ed.) *Drinking and Problem Drinking*, London, Junction, 1–22.

Shaw, S., Cartwright, A.K.J., Spratley, T.A. and Harwin, J. (1978) *Responding to Drinking Problems*, London, Croom Helm.

Shaw, S., Ottu, S. and Hashimi, L. (1985) *Problem Drinking: Experiments in Detoxification*, London, Bedford Square Press/National Council for Voluntary Organization, 150–2.

Stockwell, R., Murphy, D. and Hodgson, R. (1983) 'The Severity of Alcohol Dependence Questionnaire, its use, reliability and validity', *British Journal of Addiction* 78, 145–55.

Straus, R. and McCarthy, R.G. (1951) 'Non-addictive pathological drinking pattern of homeless men', *Quarterly Journal of Studies on Alcohol* 12, 601–11.

Straus, R. (1974) *Escape from Custody: A Study of Alcoholism and Institutional Dependency as Reflected on the Life Record of a Homeless Man*, New York, Harper and Row.

Straus, R. (1989) 'Conversation with Robert Straus'. *British Journal of Addiction* 84, 7–17.

19. Primary care for problem drug users in an area with a high rate of HIV infection

ROY ROBERTSON

INTRODUCTION

In recent years, the problem of increasing numbers of illicit drug users has been evident throughout the United Kingdom and in many other European countries (Home Office 1991). For treatment services, it is important to understand the nature of this drug-taking, as certain features, i.e. injecting drugs and types of drugs used have important implications for management. Defining the nature of problem drug use is difficult not only because the types of individuals and the localities in which drug use is prevalent have varied over the years, but also because the substances being taken change as new products become available and controls are exerted on the more traditional substances. In addition, the perception of drug use from medical points of view has changed considerably in recent years with the awareness of infections such as endocarditis, Hepatitis B, Hepatitis C and HIV infection. The introduction of HIV infection into the drug-using communities in various parts of the western world and increasingly in Asia and Oceania has concentrated medical efforts on drawing drug injectors into contact with medical services. The definition of a 'problem drug user', therefore, is extremely wide and might depend to a certain extent on the perspective from which the drug user is being viewed. Many physicians and non-medical individuals might view any illegal drug use as problematic, whereas many drug users regard their drug intake as a low-risk activity and of no major concern. Discussion in this chapter will largely be concerned with the manifestations of drug use presenting to primary care doctors and nursing staff, and, although this might often be seen as being principally caused by injecting drugs, the increasing use of oral substances, both legally and illegally obtained, will be noted. This chapter stresses aspects of primary care relevant to areas in which there is a high rate of HIV infection associated with intravenous drug use (Robertson 1986; Robertson et al. 1986).

An important development in recent years has been the trend to care in the community rather than in hospital or other institutions. This has come about for a variety of reasons but principally because of the awareness that early contact with drug users is important if prevention is to be carried out. Also, many of the traditional establishments tend to have among their clientele individuals who have been using drugs in a variety of forms for many years. The fundamental changes brought about by the development of care in the community have also given rise to new types of treatments and models of care and to a more realistic expectation that management is likely to be protracted if not long-term. Drug use, therefore, has become, for primary care, an ongoing problem fitting more comfortably with the concept of 'shared care' commonly in practice for such diseases as diabetes and hypertension rather than 'acute care' familiar in such diseases as trauma, cardiovascular problems and infections. This changing pattern of drug use has emerged over several years, brought about by political, economic and world events as well as prescribing patterns consequent on medical events outlined above.

GENERAL HEALTH ISSUES

Along with increasing awareness of the variety of substance abuse has come more understanding of the wide diversity of effects which substances taken inappropriately have on mental and physical health. Concentration on symptoms related to withdrawals of acute and severe intoxication have given rise to interest in the effects on the psyche and the behaviour of people taking stimulants, narcotics, opiates and other psychoactives. It is extremely important for general physicians to realise that drugs in these widely differing categories can have stunningly different effects on an individual behaviour and that, for example, an individual taking a stimulant such as cocaine, amphetamine or ecstasy (MDMA) will have very different problems from somebody taking a narcotic such as heroin or morphine or an individual using a sedative such as a barbiturate or benzodiazepine. To list the individual symptoms attributable to these drugs and to others is not possible within the confines of this chapter. Even so, it is emphasised that knowledge of the likely effects of drugs in different classes and local knowledge of the drug-taking scene are extremely important in effective diagnoses. In addition to the class of drug, it is important to have information about the route of administration. Drugs taken intravenously produce a maximum effect almost immediately deteriorating as time goes on, whereas drugs taken orally might be expected to have a much longer and more sustained action. Specific problems might, therefore, be related to dam-

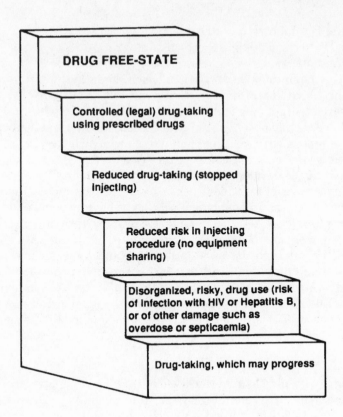

DRUG FREE-STATE

Controlled (legal) drug-taking
using prescribed drugs

Reduced drug-taking (stopped
injecting)

Reduced risk in injecting
procedure (no equipment
sharing)

Disorganized, risky, drug use (risk
of infection with HIV or Hepatitis B,
or of other damage such as
overdose or septicaemia)

Drug-taking, which may progress

Figure 19.1 Hierarchy of the aims of drug treatment.

age at injection site causing abscesses or thromboses, or to the central
effects of the drug itself such as unconsciousness, apnoea in extreme
cases and prolonged sedation in others (Ronald and Witcomb 1991 in
press). For drugs being ingested, the behavioural problems may be short
or long-acting, and experience of the effects of substances on patients
such as cannabis (marijhuana), LSD, amphetamine and narcotics is
extremely important in developing an awareness of drug problems.
General problems which may present to primary care may also include
chronic constipation with or without haemorrhoids in those abusing
narcotics chronically, weight loss and general neglect in those finding
their intake of drugs escalating beyond their economic means, and acute
injuries arising out of violence associated with the illegal drug market.
There are, of course, some specific antidotes which may be of use medically
for the treatment of different drug overdoses. The most important of
these is Naloxone (NARCAN), for the treatment of narcotic-induced unconsciousness. This can be given in repeated doses,as it is short-acting
compared with some drugs of abuse. Antagonists for benzodiazepines

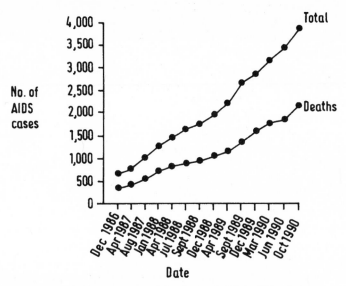

Figure 19.2 Recorded AIDS cases and deaths in the United Kingdom
(1986–90) (Department of Health 1990)

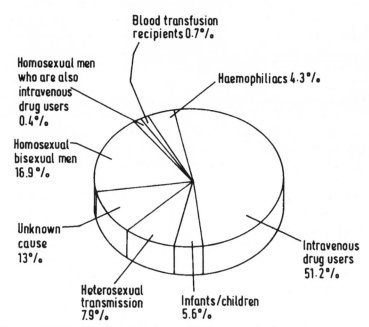

Figure 19.3 Cumulative percentages of HIV seropositive test reports in
Scotland (10 June 1990)
(Communicable Diseases (Scotland) Unit, Glasgow 1990)

are now available and may be of some clinical use, but there is little that is able to reverse the acute effects of stimulant or hallucinogen intoxication. In such cases, mild sedation might be required, although in general terms supportive therapy is more important.

DRUG-PRESCRIBING AND DETOXIFICATION

For patients, and certainly for families presenting with problems of drug use, the issue of treatment and the urgency of some sort of cure are high priorities. It is important at every stage to emphasise the nature of drug dependence or drug misuse as a disorder and the lack of a specific cure in conventional medical terms. Without being unnecessarily negative,it is vital to let individuals and families understand that relapse into drug use is common but that the general trend is towards improvement, especially when the patient is supported by family, friends and medical advisers. It is, of course, increasingly popular among members of the medical profession to use substitute drug-prescribing in an attempt to divert damaging drug use and to draw individuals into contact with helping agencies. This has been elaborated in Chapter17 and has been further discussed by the Department of Health (1991). Drugs commonly prescribed include methadone mixture, a long-acting opiate analogue which is generally taken as an oral preparation and which provides a useful alternative to the random and irregular nature of illegal drug-taking. In the UK, any doctor can prescribe methadone for a drug dependent. As an adjunct treatment, such prescribing is meant to draw patients into contact with agencies designed to improve awareness of drug problems and to provide supportive and psychological therapy for those in need.

Equally important and popular as a medical intervention is detoxification from drug-taking. This should not necessarily be seen as an alternative or a contradiction to maintenance or substitute drug-prescribing, but is currently viewed as an appropriate therapy to be attempted at times when drug users are most receptive to this form of treatment. Detoxification can be carried out in or out of residential accommodation, and, in different regions and in different countries enthusiasm for specific programs varies. There seems little doubt that residential therapy for detoxification is preferable to non- residential support, and results, at least in the short term, appear to be better. There are, however, a huge variety of prototypes and views concerning detoxification and/or longer-term treatments. Residential facilities should be available in most regions because individuals abusing drugs can change their behaviour and drug problems if subjected to such therapies. In general, it is important for physicians and general doctors to understand the remitting and relapsing nature of drug dependence as a disorder and to proceed optimistically towards the goal of long-term abstinence without necessarily being disillusioned or depressed by short-term lapses or relapses. The hierachy of the aims of drug treatment is illustrated in Figure 19.1 on page 154. Patients may remain at any level for years.

LIAISON WITH OTHER AGENCIES

In common with other chronic remitting and relapsing disorders, many professionals and support agencies might be expected to become involved with a drug user. In some cases, this can be very extensive, and, as one might expect in a disorder that may go on for many years, the range of agencies involved might require some coordination and certainly cooperation between staff. General practitioners have a traditional role in coordinating treatment packages for different disorders, and it seems logical that they should assume a pivotal role in the management of drug-related problems, especially as medical agencies becoming increasingly involved in recent years. It might, therefore, be necessary for the GP to be in touch with or refer individual drug users to a variety of medical agencies, including infectious diseases specialists, genito-urinary medicine and at times general medicine and surgery. Additionally, there are an increasing range of statutory and non-statutory agencies working with problem drug users, especially in city-centre practices, which may find themselves in contact with social work departments and non-statutory drug agencies who have a specific remit to support clients through crises and through longer-term social and domestic drug-related problems. Increasingly, inner-city GPs might be involved with the legal frame-work as their individual patients become involved with the police and law enforcement agencies. Confidentiality should not be used as an excuse to avoid constructive involvement with such organizations with the permission of the patient. There is an important role for GPs formulating policies and guiding treatment services in the community, especially as general health care moves into a new era of highlighted community care. Without appropriate pressure from primary care to attract resources into areas of need, the traditional model of hospital-based treatment services is likely to persist,and what is considered by many to be more appropriate community care may fail to develop. To a certain extent,the multiple problems of drug users have to be addressed by a multi-disciplinary team,and the presence of individuals with social work knowledge, welfare rights experience and abilities to support clients over long periods of time is indispensable. It is far better to work as part of an extended primary care team in addressing such multitfaceted problems rather than attempt to develop expertise in many of these extremely difficult and non-medical areas.

DIAGNOSIS AND COUNSELLING FOR HIV INFECTION

The Human Immunodeficiency Virus has attracted the headlines as a problem for drug users in recent years and undoubtedly has been the major recent incentive for the development of drug treatment services in Scotland and in many other areas (Robertson 1992). Figure 19.2 indicates the rise in UK AIDS cases between 1986 and 1990. Figure 19.3 shows the distribution of the means of transmission among those tested as HIV-infected in Scotland.

It is important, therefore, that GPs and other members of the primary care team understand the importance of assessing HIV risk, making a diagnosis and counselling patients. Clearly, drug users are at risk not just because of drug injecting but also sexually, as are the rest of the sexually active population (Strang and Stimson 1990). It is thus important to recognise that,in assessing risk, both these areas have to be taken into account. in attempting to reduce the risk, safe sex advice and provision of condoms and contraceptive information are as important as the provision of sterile injecting equipment and instruction about sterile techniques. The clinical aspects of HIV/AIDS among drug users have already been discussed in some detail in Chapter 7. All GPs must be in an ideal position to carry out simple tasks and instructions in order to minimise HIV/AIDS risks among problem drug users. It is hoped that this will develop as a normal extension to the primary care workload. Counselling about HIV risk and testing for HIV antibodies need not be complicated, and in the past perhaps has been made unnecessarily so. It is extremely important that the doctor or nurse should understand clearly the level of risk before advising or suggesting an HIV antibody test and should have a clear understanding of the nature of the test and the implications of a positive result. Many excellent publications are available for medical staff as well as for patients (e.g. Green 1989; Juengst 1989). After some discussion, patients should be encouraged to read about the issues before making a final decision about whether or not to have a test. It is common for individuals to present late in the course of a disease, and of course an HIV antibody test is not itself of any use in identifying how long the virus has been present unless there is a clear history or manifestation of a recent seroconversion illness or clinical signs of advanced disease. Seroconversion illnesses classically take the form of an acute viral infection not unlike glandular fever,with marked pharyngitis and sometimes purulent tonsillitis associated with a widespread macular rash, fever and myalgia. It is more common, however, for individuals to present having a history of risky activities and for positive tests in these individuals to indicate the presence of the virus without there being any way of accurately dating this. In those found to be HIV antibody positive, additional testing such as the use of full blood counts and lymphocyte sub-sets can give a clearer indication of the likely stage of the illness. This, when taken in association with clinical findings such as persistent generalised swollen lymph glands or the presence of the widespread clinical problems described below, can be used to ascertain the stage of the illness and to counsel the patient as to whether or not treatment is required.

HIV-RELATED CLINCAL PROBLEMS

Medical manifestations of HIV and AIDS might be best considered under the various categories outlined in the Centers for Disease Control Classification of AIDS. These have been elaborated in Chapter 7. Stage I indicates seroconversion illness already described, and, if this is severe enough to present to doctors, it is usually seen within a few weeks of infection taking place. It is, however, more common for this to pass as an unnoticed viral type of infection and for presentation to be because of the perceived risk or at a later stage when advance symptoms develop. Stage II is of asymptomatic infection and can last for many years. During this stage,there may be no clinical signs, although the presence of a positive test might give rise to profound and persistent psychological problems which require considerable time and resources in their management. Stage III is that of persistent generalised lymphadenopathy. The patient may be comparatively free of severe symptoms, and this is most commonly a diagnosis arising from physical examination rather than by history-taking. Swollen glands may be evident, and may at times be large and painless in the usual areas but may also be present in parts of the body where lymph glands are not usually easily palpable. Stage IV, or full-blown AIDS, is the stage at which most medical intervention is required and during which time treatment may be intensive or latterly merely supportive. Patients may, for example, require recurrent and repeated treatments for seborrhoeic skin conditions, for fungal skin, nail and throat infections and for repeated chest and other infections which respond to simple and easily prescribed drugs. The use of appropriate anti fungal shampoos, a range of antifungal throat pastilles, lozenges and systemic antifungal agents and a wide variety of skin emollients and creams is essential. Symptomatic treatment is, at many times, all that may be available for chronic irritations, diarrhoea and weight loss. Dietary supplements and vitamin replacements should be instituted early. Herpetic lesions, both herpes simplex and herpes zoster, can be treated aggressively by GPs with topical and systemic antiviral drugs.

The development of specific antiviral agents for HIV infection may not seem to be an appropriate topic for general practice. It is, however, increasingly common for patients to choose maintenance therapy in the community rather than hospitalisation or even attending outpatient departments. General practitioners, therefore, should understand that treatments are now available or becoming available which have a specific antiviral activity and are likely to have a product licence for treatment of early as well as late disease. Specifically, AZT (Zidovudine,

Retrovir) is a drug which was originally thought to be dangerously toxic but which is now regarded as first-line treatment for advancing HIV infection. Since 1990, the drug has a product licence for early asymptomatic disease in individuals who have a deteriorating lymphocyte count. Earlier still, the drug was available and continues to be available for treatment of advancing HIV infection in the presence of symptoms of full-blown AIDS. Although much optimism has been put forward for the use of this drug, it does seem to have a use limited to prolonging the course of the disease by eighteen months to two years. This seems to be largely independent of when the drug is first taken, and the rationale for prescribing early is based on the enthusiasm for prolonging the asymptomatic period rather than prolonging the time of life when symptoms are increasingly severe. Understanding the use of this drug and discussing this with patients must be an important part of managing the overall problem. Newer drugs such as DDI (Dideoxyinosine) and many others are increasingly available under trial conditions and are likely to be in much more use in the next few years.

CONCLUSIONS

There are enormous areas of involvement for those doctors and primary care team members willing to take an interest. Drug users, far from being exclusively manipulative, violent and antisocial, provide a rewarding and fulfilling patient or client group who present with a challenging array of clinical and psychological problems. Understanding these problems is an important prerequisite for treatment, and being aware of the limitations of medical intervention can save the difficulties of being drawn into areas which are unfamiliar. Liaison with hospital and other support agencies is critically important, not just for the benefit of the patient but also to support the primary care team and to prevent such difficulties. General practitioners have a singular responsibility for managing problem drug users and for the wider preventative initiatives in young people drawn into drug use and placed consequently at risk of HIV infection and other equally serious and fatal disorders.

REFERENCES

Communicable Diseases (Scotland) Office, Ruchill Hospital, Scotland (1990) Personal Communication.
Department of Health (1991) *Drug Misuse and Dependence: Guidelines on Clinical Management*, London, Department of Health.
Department of Health (1991) Personal Communication.
Green, J. (1989) 'Counselling in HIV infection and AIDS', in Miller, D., Wiben, J. and Green, J. (eds) *Management of HIV infections*, London, Macmillan Press.
Home Office (1991) *Statistics of the Misuse of Drugs in the United Kingdom*, London

Juengst, E.T. and Koenig, B.A. (eds) (1989) *The meaning of AIDS,* Praeger Press, New York.

Robertson, J.R. (1986) *Heroin, AIDS and Society*, London, Hodder and Stoughton

Robertson, J.R., Bucknall, A.B.V., Welsby, P.D. et al. (1986) 'Epidemic of HTLV3/LAV infection among intravenous drug users', *British Medical Journal* 292, 527-9.

Robertson, J.R. (1990) 'The arrival of HIV' in Strang, J. and Gossop, M. (eds) *Responding to Drug Misuse: The British System*, Oxford, Oxford University Press (in press).

Ronald, P., Witcomb, J.C. and Robertson, J.R. (1992) 'Problems of Drug Abuse, HIV and AIDS', *British Journal of General Practitioners* (in press).

Strang, J. and Stimson, G.V. (eds) (1990) *AIDS and Drug Misuse*, London, Tavistock / Routledge.

20. Alcohol and drug problems in prisons

JOHN PEARCE

The Scottish Prison Service consists of twenty-one penal establishments and a central headquarters in Edinburgh. Population levels have fluctuated in recent years: they peaked in 1986 at approximately 5,500 and in 1991 have been running slightly below 5,000.

Incarceration rates are regarded as very high in European terms and, having reached approximately 110 per 100,000, have settled recently to slightly below 100 per 100,000.

There has been a surge in the imprisonment of men for sentences over eighteen months, and this group represents about forty per cent of the total population. The 'Lifer' group (those serving life sentences) represents about ten per cent of the total prison population which is fifty per cent higher than that in England and Wales, where there is a separate prison service operating within a different judicial system.

The Scottish Office Home and Health Department publishes an annual 'Prisons in Scotland' report within which is a chapter on 'Health, Safety and Hygiene'.

Over the past few years, treatment for prisoners with substance misuse problems has increased, although, interestingly, alcohol dependence appears to be in decline among men. This is indicated by Table 20.1.

In a study conducted throughout the Scottish prisons in 1990, 27.5 per cent of respondents indicated past intravenous drug misuse and 7.7 per cent of respondents indicated past intravenous drug misuse *while in prison* (Power et al. 1991).

ILLICIT SUBSTANCES IN SCOTTISH PRISONS

The last twenty years have seen enormous changes within the sub-culture of Scottish prisons in comparison with the previous two decades. The volume and pace of change have particularly accelerated during the past decade which has been characterised by increasing challenge to authority,

		1984	1985	1986	1987	1988–9	1989–90
'Drug Abuse'	Males	935	1,104	1437	1,358	1,659	2,301
	Females	228	256				
Alcohol Dependence	Males	1,560	1,165	649	624	648	547
	Females	139	170	167	127	164	121
Average daily prison population		4,753	5,273	5,588	5,446	5,415	4,886

The years 1986, 1987, 1988–9 and 1989–90 are totals. Variations in statistical categories over these years create difficulties in presenting a simple table.

Table 20.1 Drug and alcohol misuse in Scottish prisons, 1984–90

initially by assertive litigation and in the second half of the decade by increasingly violent attacks on property and staff, culminating in a sustained series of very serious hostage incidents. Throughout these incidents, there has been extensive damage to prison property and concomitant disruption of the prison routine, resulting in pressure on both staff and prisoners. It has been evident that illicit drugs have frequently featured either as part of the subcultural power base or as a specific problem within the siege area itself.

For the greater part of the twentieth century the main illicit drug in Scottish prisons has been alcohol, while the main licit drug has been tobacco. The former has been acquired by smuggling of various kinds or has been produced via home-brew techniques. Tobacco has been obtained by use of wages earned in prison workshops and spent at the prison shop or again by smuggling. The 'tobacco baron' during this period was a constant feature, payment being made either inside or outside the prison at extortionate rates in cash or by services rendered within the prison ranging from carrying a share of the 'bank' through to enforcement by violence.

In many ways, the market was restricted by the ability to pay and by the actual supply of both alcohol and tobacco, which are bulky items. Certainly, some of the noxious combinations of yeast, vegetable peelings, sugar and water and the very thin cigarettes, hand-rolled and passed avidly around, did not give support to a view other than that the illicit activity was emphasised by scarcity rather than quality.

Inevitably there were occasional 'addicts', some registered and some not, and these were commonly users of heroin. During the 1960s and 1970s, there were the well-known individuals who popped pills or 'goof-balls' as they were termed in prison argot. However, by far the greatest problem was the significant number of prisoners who had serious difficulties in the community with alcohol. One feature of drink-ing has been the Scottish practice of 'buying rounds' or, among younger drinkers, passing round bottles of cheap wine. It has been argued that this very strongly ingrained sub-cultural practice has been the precursor to the explosion of HIV infection attributable to sharing infected injecting equipment.

During the 1980s a rapid growth in drug misuse in prison was evident in many communities. There had in the past been small outbreaks of LSD use, highlighting specific features of the new drug culture in the outside community. These were, simply, of high value; very small-sized doses and easily hidden.

LSD was particularly difficult to detect due to the use of microdots hidden in a magazine or under postage stamps on letters or a page edge soaked in a solution. This was to be the start of highly ingenious and inventive ways to deliver high-demand, high value products. The explo-sion in the community in Scotland of the misuse of prescription drugs was reflected in prisons during the 1980s by a strong demand for these drugs by incarcerated prisoners. Some of these were dependent upon prescribed drugs and usually used such substances intravenously.

At the same time, the increasing volume of cannabis available, virtually on demand, on the streets of Scottish cities and large towns has been paralleled by a pro rata increase in availability and use within the prisons. The power has inexorably moved from the tobacco barons to those who can provide a range of prescription drugs (normally ben-zodiazepines, opiate painkillers) or cannabis. The high values involved require cash payment outside, creating problems for families during the sentence and for the individual prisoner while in prison or on release if payment fails to keep up with usage. A single tablet of Temgesic (Bu-prenorphine) may cost almost the equivalent of a full week's prison pay.

It is a feature of the modern prison in Scotland that there are effectively two types of demand. First, there is the urgent polydrug quest of the regular misuser. The second type of demand is the more planned and considered recreational use, perhaps during weekend lock-up, of cannabis, LSD or 'snorted' Temgesic.

RESPONSE IN SECURITY TERMS

The influence of drug suppliers on the prison subculture has had an impact on order and discipline. This has inevitably led to an increase in security responses designed to deter would-be smugglers by increased risk of capture. Contraband practices may involve some prisoners and their families being bullied into smuggling in drugs during visits. In Scotland there are many 'open visits', during which objects may be passed across an open table. Smuggling sometimes includes the carry-ing-in of drugs secreted in anal passages by prisoners working in the community as part of pre-release programmes. The latter may be unwilling, but heavily pressurised, individuals who may not be drug users themselves.

An increasingly common practice is reported to be for regular drug users, who know they will be remanded in custody or expect a custodial sentence at their court appearance, either to swallow drugs in a condom or to pack their rectums with drugs wrapped in cling film. This latter practice may also include a modern small syringe. Currently, there is no routine searching of anal cavities by Scottish Prison Service staff.

Much the most persistent contraband route is during the visit. Naturally this has been the focus of attention in all Scottish prisons. Closed-circuit television surveillance with concomitant video recording facilities, increased numbers of visit supervisory staff and also staff to carry out strip searches post-visit, are an increasing drain on finite resources. Those caught or clearly consistently attempting to avoid surveillance may be thereafter restricted to special closed visit areas where a glass screen separates family and friends from the prisoner and where communication is via a microphone device. This is a constant source of friction but is regrettably necessary. In late 1990, two separate court convictions involved mothers passing or attempting to pass small packages of drugs from mouth to mouth to their adult sons.

The practice of swallowing small clingfilm-covered packages is a particularly difficult problem which, short of draconian surveillance, can generally only be resolved by recourse to 'closed visits'.

The most recent innovation in the security response has been the use of sniffer dogs. Scotland's prisons have one team of a handler and two dogs, with a second team in training, who are flexibly deployed to random searching and to specific target searching of establishments. Dogs are generally utilised in sweeps of accommodation and work areas. In addition, the appearance of a dog at the entrance to a visit-room area can have a remarkable impact on both the composure of some visitors and the incidence of small packages being found on the floor in the area just before the visitors pass the dog.

It should, however, be noted that there is an increasing dissociation by the majority of visitors from the determined minority. Within the past couple of years, the mood in visit areas when a staff team intervenes at a suspected visit has changed from the frank hostility of subcultural solidarity to the clear body language of denial of support. Clearly, the threat to the quality of prison visits by the actions of a minority has caused a degree of rejection of such individuals by other visitors.

An increasing feature has been the growing liaison by the prisons with police drug units and intelligence units. Such liaison attempts to monitor the actions of the more organised suppliers and regrettably, but necessarily, to check out the allegations of staff involvement as carriers of contraband. The latter involves very small numbers of staff, but the manipulative, subversive and sophisticated prisoner has a lot of time to probe weaknesses, to entrap and to pressurise the member of staff who is vulnerable through lack of experience, personal greed or indeed through his own personal use of illegal substances such as cannabis.

RESPONSE TO HIV/AIDS

There is perhaps no place in the world quite so vulnerable to anxiety and hysteria about HIV/AIDS as the closed environment of a prison. Many of the responses by prison services across the world have been, at the least, to compartmentalise hygienically and segregate the known or suspected HIV seropositive prisoner into hospital-type areas. Even worse has been the development of prejudiced and vindictive regimes which have ignored accepted standards in the panic to put the problem out of sight and out of mind into virtual ghettos within penal establishments.

The Scottish Prison Service experience has been that such marginalised and isolated groups (for whatever reason segregated) have tended to create more problems than such a process solves. In the mid to late 1980s, the instinct, in the face of a rising tide of HIV infection in the drug-misusing community, was to take a positive stance against segregation. This has been refined into a sophisticated multidisciplinary approach including community agencies, so that in 1991, based on an expanded role of trained and enthusiastic uniformed prison officers, highly supportive, interactive programmes were in place to the benefit of prisoner and staff. There is not the scope within this short chapter to detail the process, but the outcomes have included a respite, care and support facility within Saughton Prison in Edinburgh, a national two-day conference of invited expert delegates including prisoners held within a prison, a mass voluntary and anonymous HIV screening event using saliva swabs (achieving eighty per cent response) and, perhaps most notably, a four-day residential Life, Death and Transition Workshop run by AIDS specialist Elisabeth Kubler-Ross (Kubler-Ross 1987) in Saughton Prison involving male and female prisoners, infected and non-infected prisoners, male and female staff and male and female community resource individuals.

DEVELOPMENT FROM THE LESSONS LEARNED IN HIV/AIDS WORK

The period between 1988 and mid-1991 involved intensive co-operation from all levels of the community and all sections of the prison staff and prisoners. The Scottish Prison Service's problem of HIV/AIDS lies principally among young heterosexual adult, intravenous drug misusers. This group was typically infected in the early to mid-1980s when knowledge of HIV/AIDS was limited. They shared scarce injecting equipment in 'shooting galleries' utilising prescription drugs such as benzodiazepines and opiate painkillers (Robertson and Bucknall 1986; Robertson et al. 1986). This activity centred on three main cities, Glasgow, Dundee and Edinburgh. The epidemiology of the HIV/AIDS epidemic in Scotland has been described in Chapter 6.

In mid-1988, the Scottish Prison Service as a whole had about fifteen times as many cases of HIV infection per thousand prisoners as did the Prison Service of England and Wales. Saughton Prison had as many HIV-infected inmates as did all of the prisons in England and Wales together. In the short-term and remand accommodation halls, this peaked with one in four of all prisoners being known to be HIV-seropositive.

The involvement of uniformed prison staff, specialist staff and community agencies with this intense concentration resulted in constructive networking, increased confidence within the prison team of their ability to deal with sensitive and controversial issues and above all a growing forum for prisoners and staff to work cooperatively together.

The initial tasks for the Scottish Prison Service were to cope with and dispel the initial anxiety and hysteria associated with HIV/AIDS, and to set up educational and support and care programmes. During 1990, the focus of activity turned to methods of minimising drug-related harm.

DRUG MISUSE IN SAUGHTON PRISON

It is worthwhile to describe the drug-misusing problem in Edinburgh's Saughton Prison in mid-1991. A total of seventy-four prisoners in this institution were known to be drug-misusers. Two thirds were aged under thirty. Only eighteen of these were serving or had served a sentence for a drugs offence. Thirty-three prisoners were serving sentences for drug offences. Only about one third were noted as misusers of drugs other than cannabis.

The past three years have seen a marked change in the reported use of injecting equipment, both inside and outside the prison, and in observed needle marks either on reception or during routine medical examinations. Prisoners report much less injected drug use, and also report less sharing and greater cleaning of injecting equpiment. In 1988, twenty-five sets of injecting equipment were discovered during searches in the prison, in 1989 two sets were discovered and in 1990 only one was discovered. This pattern is confirmed by anecdote, specific intelligence, medical examination and by Dye and Isaacs (1991).

Saughton Prison contains a considerable number of young men who, before admission, have misused a wide range of substances, broadly described as 'prescription drugs' *plus* a limited amount of heroin. Cannabis is also so widely used that drug-takers tend not to report its use, thereby almost putting it at an equivalent level with tobacco. These drug misusers are typically drawn from a delinquent subculture who are commonly involved in a range of criminal activities.

THE HARM-MINIMISATION APPROACH

It is clear, therefore, that a significant proportion of the admissions to the prison, principally on remand or on sentences ranging up to eighteen months, have regularly misused drugs and may encounter withdrawal symptoms at various levels from physical to psychological. This inevitably generates illicit activity, sub-cultural and peer-group problems and friction with authority.

Building on the very good community networks developed from HIV/AIDS work, it has therefore been approved at government ministerial level that Saughton Prison should institute a pilot drug-reduction programme. This scheme will aim to return prisoners to the community drug-free, well informed and well supported. The pilot project has been designed in conjunction with drug agencies and medical services in the community, prison officers and specialists on the staff of the prison. A crucial element has been the need to deal with abuse of prescription drugs and the existence of a strong ethos in Lothian Region of methadone maintenance sponsored by the Community Drug Problem Service and managed by individual general practitioners. The latter is described in Chapter 17. Close cooperation will be necessary between the medical and nursing services of both the community and the prison in setting initial prescription dosages. Similar cooperation will be necessary between the drug agency workers and social workers outside the prison and the various prison staff who provide educational and social support. It is intended that the process will be one of 'through care' with outside agencies closely involved post-admission and pre-release.

The implementation of this scheme will take account of the extensive misuse of Benzodiazepines in Lothian and of the established usage in that locality of Methadone maintenance. The Reduction Programme will be voluntary, and, in those cases where prisoners choose on admission *not* to join the programme, they will, nonetheless, have access to support during a shorter detoxification programme.

The Reduction Programme itself will cover a period of twenty-eight days for each problem drug user. The first fourteen days will be based in the prison hospital, the initial period focusing on the management of withdrawal. Drug support will be modelled on a fairly sharp reduction over the first seven to ten days followed by a long, slow tailing-off which will ease the longer pressure of Benzodiazepine withdrawal and withdrawal from methadone.

In general terms, taking account of ease of medical management, methadone maintenance will be the prime form of management, although medical staff will have the option to prescribe other drugs (such as DF 118s) during withdrawal. Some prisoners are serving sentences in place of unpaid fines. These can effect their release by payment of the money owed. It will be prudent not to introduce such individuals to methadone as a routine response but rather to prescribe a specific and appropriate support.

As already noted, the programme is voluntary and will endeavour actively to engage the prisoners involved. One-to-one counselling, educational group working and peer support groups will all enable both prison staff and drug workers from the community to build relationships with prisoners during the initial twenty-eight-day programme and throughout their sentences.

The key elements therefore will be:
- a sensitive and humane programme of withdrawal
- an educational programme involving a multidisciplinary team and utilising community drug team workers
- intensive group work
- one-to-one counselling
- peer support groups
- pre-release liaison with community drug groups
- a view that it will be for the prisoner, at release, to make a decision about continued drug use, the responsibility of the prison staff being to enable drug using prisoners to make balanced judgements from a position of being drug-free, supported and informed.

Accommodation and employment on release will be key issues, both of self-esteem and practicality, and will feature strongly in pre-release groups and presentations.

CONCLUSION

A brief and selective account has been provided of the response by the Scottish Prison Service and Saughton Prison to the vexed problem of drug misuse in prison. What is happening is evolutionary rather than revolutionary in the sense that much has been painstakingly built upon the foundation of mutual confidence between staff and prisoners which has been generated in response to the HIV/AIDS threat.

If there is to be a model set out, then it must be that support to the essential interaction between prisoner and the management of drug-dependence in prison is a prelude to return to the community. Therefore it is essential to involve community agencies with prison staff in the operation of the pilot reduction programme. Such involvement is essential to the continuation of support for problem drug users following their release from prison.

REFERENCES

Dye, S. and Isaacs, C. (1991) 'Intravenous drug misuse among prison inmates:
    implications for spread of HIV', *British Medical Journal* 302, 1506–70.
Kubler-Ross, E. (1987) *AIDS: The Ultimate Challenge*, New York, Macmillan.
Power, K.G., Markova, I., Rowlands, A., McKee, K.J., Anslow, P.J. and Kilfedder,
    C. (1991) 'Sexual behaviour in Scottish prisons', *British Medical Journal* 302,
    1507–8.
Robertson, J.R. and Bucknall, A.B.V. (1985) 'Heroin users: notifiable to the Home
    Office addicts index by general practitioners', *British Medical Journal* 291,
    111–3.
Robertson, J.R., Bucknall, A.B.V., Welsby, P.D. et al. (1986) 'Epidemic of
    AIDS-related (HTLV) infection among intravenous drug users', *British Medical
    Journal* 292, 527–9.

21. Evaluation of treatment for alcohol dependence: Avoiding methodological pitfalls

JONATHAN CHICK

INTRODUCTION

Treatments old and new are often introduced and championed in an uncritical way. If sensible choices are to be made about treatment policies, we need to improve our criteria for evaluation. This chapter principally examines some of the requirements for evaluation of alcohol treatments, although many of the issues are equally relevant for all forms of therapy in the substance misuse field.

Emrick (1975) reviewed 384 studies of the outcome in treated alcohol dependence and abuse. Miller and Hester (1986) extended the review to cover more than 400 studies. There were a small number of studies of psychological treatments which showed an advantage in adding a specific therapy to a general package of counselling (e.g. Chaney et al. 1978), but it seemed difficult to show that intensive treatment could improve on the outcome of less intensive treatments. However, these authors rejected on methodological grounds a majority of the evaluation studies which they reviewed.

Reviews of pharmacological approaches to improving the outcome of newly abstinent, detoxified patients have mostly also failed to find evidence of efficacy (Sinclair 1987; Liskow and Goodwin 1987). Disulfiram had some support in controlled studies when compliance was assured by supervision (Azrin et al. 1982; Gerrein et al. 1973; Chick et al. in press). Some benefits have been attributed to drugs acting on neurotransmitter substances in the brain. One of these is the GABA – agonist Acamprosate, which over three months, has been shown to improve outcome (Lhuintre et al. 1990). Also, in anxious or depressed patients after alcohol detoxification, the dopamine antagonist, tiapride, appears to be of help (Shaw et al. 1987).

Partly as a result of the disappointing treatment evaluation literature, some researchers have diverted attention away from short-term follow-up of six to twelve months, to long-term studies in which little or no attempt is made to evaluate the effect of treatment. Instead, attempts are made to understand the interweaving of restorative and healing processes in the environment with the characteristics of the drinker (Edwards 1989). From a humanistic point of view, this can be revealing and challenging (Vaillant 1988), but it often needs to fall back on individual case histories (Edwards 1989).

However, patients and their families, as well as referring agents including physicians and surgeons, request treatment. Large sums are spent in providing such treatment, often with no proof that it is effective (Miller 1987). Depending somewhat on the selection of patients into treatment, serious relapse can be expected in the first six months in between twenty to eighty per cent of patients treated. There is a need for new treatments, but evaluation must be rigorous. The following are suggested criteria for adequate evaluations in the treatment of alcohol dependence. Some are specific to alcohol studies, but most apply to the conduct of all studies of medical and psychological treatment. The randomised study with a control group and blind evaluation is the best way to reduce bias in assessing treatment. In the treatment of alcohol dependence, it has sometimes proved difficult to set up such studies (Andreasson et al. 1990).

CRITERIA FOR ADEQUATE EVALUATIONS IN ALCOHOL DEPENDENCE TREATMENT

A: Description of the sample

In order to be able to generalise from one treatment situation to another, and to extend the capacity to match patients to treatments, it is vital to have a description of patient characteristics in a number of respects:

(i) *The source of the sample* should be specified. The patients may be self-referred or referred for treatment by employers, doctors or community agencies, or recruited via screening a population of patients or members of the general population. Also to be specified are the patients' characteristics, particularly in terms of alcohol consumption, level of dependence on alcohol and range and extent of problems. Although the internationally used diagnostic classification systems do not fit with the preferences of all clinicians in this field, it is helpful to apply one or both classifications to the sample studies, i.e. the DSM III – R (American Medical Association 1989) or ICD 9 (World Health Organization 1978), using a checklist perhaps (ICD 10 soon to be published). There is a wide range of problem drinkers who attend clinics for treatment, but narrowing the sample to some subgroups (e.g. 'only dependent drinkers') is acceptable as long as the criteria are described.

(ii) *Measurement of co-morbidity*. Alcohol dependence or abuse may be accompanied by other psychiatric illnesses, which may pre-date the conditions or result from it: for example depression, anxiety or antisocial personality disorder (though this latter is a less widely accepted term). Assessment of these conditions should be made after detoxification, because during the heavy drinking period and during withdrawal many signs of depression and anxiety are present, which are transient (e.g. Brown and Shuckit 1988). This area is important because of evidence that different associated diagnoses influence response to different types of treatment in different ways (e.g. Kadden et al. 1989).

(iii) *Obtaining matched groups* The predictors of outcome in alcohol dependence are not known with certainty and probably interact in a complex way with treatment and treatment compliance (Edwards 1989). Randomisation is therefore greatly preferable to any other way of obtaining matched groups.

B. Randomisation

The object of randomisation is that the groups should be well matched. Allocation should be performed after intake data is collected and thus be unknown to the worker who collects the baseline measurements. In settings where social class and marital state are probable predictors of outcome, the randomisation procedure may be conducted by stratifying for these variables. *Should the study group or sample exclude patients who are not willing at the onset to follow one or other of the treatment options to which they may be randomly allocated?* A study which meets normal standards of ethical acceptability will by definition exclude some patients, since all the treatment alternatives to be compared will have been described to the patient. The problem of how to accommodate patients who default from the treatment once the study is in progress is discussed below.

C. Measuring outcome

(i) There is an advantage in repeating the same measures at intake and at follow-up so that measures of outcome can include difference scores. This helps to deal with bias arising due to imbalances between groups which may have occurred despite randomisation. Using scales sensitive to change reveals treatment effects. For example, asking patients about being late for work or absent from work through drinking, will reveal more incidents than dismissal from work which is a rarer type of event.

(ii) *Consumption measures:* The reliability of self-reported data on alcohol consumption is rightly questioned. Although studies show that such data correlate fairly well with data for the same time period collected from patients' relatives, this is only partly reassuring (Babor et al. 1987; Midanik et al. 1989). Unreliability due to forgetting can be reduced by frequent, e.g. monthly, interviews with the research worker. But this will not reduce unreliability due to lying or deliberate minimisation, or unreliability of the informant's report because the drinker has hidden the drinking. The measure of drinking should include an estimate of quantity per day, or per session, as well as overall quantity, since certain types of harm are associated with heavy sessional intake (e.g. injuries, violence, gastritis) rather than continuous drinking. It is worth recording the pattern of drinking over a six- or twelve-month period. Has it been mainly continuous, or mainly at weekends, or long periods of sobriety interspersed with binges?

Objective markers of alcohol intake should be used. Alcohol in the blood, breath or urine at all follow-up contact with the patient can be measured. Blood tests such as MCV (mean red cell volume) and gamma glutamyl transpeptidase (gamma GT) or aspartate transaminase (AST) have a role. In the general population, they correlate fairly well with self-reported alcohol intake (Chick, Kreitman and Plant 1981). The strength of correlations diminishes progressively as one moves from general practice to general hospital samples (Lloyd et al. 1982) and to alcohol treatment unit samples (Potamianos et al. 1985; Latcham 1986). The tests also work better in cultures such as southern Europe, where daily drinking is the norm. This is because these tests, especially the MCV, are elevated only from sustained heavy drinking, and many patients sufficiently impaired to attend alcohol treatment units have already begun to have periods of abstinence albeit with bouts of heavy drinking (Bell and Steensland 1987).

However, Keso and Salaspuro (1990), analysing their outcome data with and without markers, emphasise the great importance of objective tests, without which twenty per cent of patients are wrongly classified as having a good outcome. Blood tests have been criticised as being of only limited value as screening tests, because some thirty per cent of clinic attenders have normal values. But for those drinkers whose tests are abnormal at intake to treatment and normalise with detoxification, sustained periods of future drinking will be revealed. And even within 'normal' limits gamma GT will rise and fall with changes in alcohol consumption. It may be that the carbohydrate-deficient transferrin test (CDT) (e.g. Storey et al. 1987) will come to complement MCV and gamma GT, but this test is not routinely available.

(iii) The alcohol problems treatment literature now requires more than alcohol consumption data. Rather than abstinence alone, many therapists in this field have as their goal a reduction of problems and enhancement of health and personal and social functioning. This may also be nearer to patients' goals too, for many of whom intentions to abstain from alcohol fluctuate greatly.

Self-reports must be supplemented by reports of third parties (relative, employer, family doctor, local authority social worker etc.) and an examination of records, e.g. hospital records or, if accessible, police or court information, centrally-held sickness records (e.g. Kristensson et al. 1983) or sickness benefit claims (e.g. Nordstrom and Bergland 1987).

It may be appropriate only to recruit subjects for whom collateral information is available (e.g. Chick et al. 1988). However, this will diminish the generalisability of findings to patients with little or no social support.

The instrument used to enquire into alcohol-related problems will have face validity, and there is no best instrument. It should cover the range of areas, relevant to the culture of the population under study, of health and social functioning, including for example police trouble and trouble at work or in the family (e.g. Drummond et al. 1990).

(iv) *The importance of blind assessment*: Patients may wish to please researchers and may gloss over continuing difficulties. If patients remain blind to the type of treatment they are receiving (as could be the case in a trial of medication), then such bias will not result in favouring the test assessment. But it may be difficult for patients and assessors to remain blind, and thus self-reports or assessors' reports *must* be backed up by collateral and objective evidence. Also questions should not be asked by the assessor about the patient's experience of the treatment, since that could remove the assessor's blindness.

D. Follow-up

Alcohol dependents are among the most difficult patient populations to follow up. Their condition results in family break-up, loss of accommodation and loss of job. They may be ambivalent about being involved in treatment in the first place. At intake to the study, auxiliary follow-up addresses (of friends and relatives) should be obtained.

Eighty per cent or more one-year follow-up has been obtained with perseverance in a number of studies of chronic alcohol dependent populations. If suitable follow-up personnel are chosen, blood test data can be obtained on at least ninety per cent of those contacted (Chick, Lloyd and Crombie 1985).

Loss to follow-up: patients who are difficult to follow up tend to have worse outcome (Moos and Bliss 1978; Mackenzie et al. 1987). Thus, it is not acceptable, as happened in one recent report (Barrucand, Paille and Gillet 1987), to apportion non-contacts to an outcome category according to the distribution of outcome categories in the study as a whole. By doing this, the authors obtained a statistically significant three-month outcome advantage for the test treatment, which disappeared when non-contacts were omitted from the analysis or were allocated to a poor-outcome category.

E. Non-compliance

Compliance with treatment is at the heart of therapy for alcohol abuse and alcohol dependence. Dropping out of treatment is very common. The patient's motivation to do something about himself and his drinking fluctuates. Partly this reflects the despair and hopelessness of some of the clients who find their way to clinics. It has also to do with the pleasure, or relief, which they get from drinking. Part of the skill of the therapist is in helping patients consolidate the motivation to do something about their drinking. But clients may also reject treatment because they feel it is inappropriate or because of adverse effects ascribed to the treatment. Because these factors cannot be disentangled, many feel it is correct to analyse results retaining subjects in the 'intention to treat' group. However, it has been argued (Hore 1988) that in alcohol dependence treatment research, as in some other types of clinical trial, it is unfair to a treatment to draw conclusions based on outcome of patients who, although allocated to it, have not had that treatment. Two recent studies have attempted to look separately at compliers and non-compliers. Fawcett et al. (1986), in a double-blind study of lithium, randomly allocated 104 newly discharged alcoholics to daily lithium carbonate or placebo. The 'survival curve' in terms of remaining completely abstinent was almost the same in both groups. However, those in the lithium group who maintained a serum lithium level at or above 0.4 mmol did much better than those in the lithium group who did not maintain that serum lithium level or who admitted to taking their medication less than half the time – sixty-three per cent still abstinent at one year compared with nineteen per cent. The compliant patients in the placebo group, i.e. those who apparently took their pills, also did well, with forty-two per cent abstinent at one year. However, they did less well than those experiencing a therapeutic level of lithium for most of the time. Unfortunately, this study could not refute the possibility that the group with the therapeutic levels of lithium was simply the purest group in terms of compliance; no physiological marker was used to index placebo-taking, so the most compliant placebo group subjects could not be studied separately.

Fuller et al. (1986) randomly assigned 605 newly abstinent patients to 250 mgs Disulfiram or to placebo groups. All medications were marked with riboflavin so that at the clinic visits compliance could be checked by urine tests. Of 577 who finished the study, twenty per cent were rated compliant. Of the compliant patients forty-three per cent completed a year's abstinence compared to eight per cent of the non-compliant patients. Approximately the same percentage of compliant patients were found in each group, and, irrespective of treatment given, the abstinence rate was the same in each group of compliant patients. Similarly among the 315 non-compliant patients there were no differences between groups on the criterion of one year's abstinence. The authors state:

> we designed our study to accept patients without first having a trial period in which they demonstrated adherence to the Disulfiram regimen because we wanted our study to be generalisable to the usual clinical situation in which it is not known how faithfully patients will take their medication when they are first given it.

When these authors separately analysed data on total drinking days in the year's follow-up which could only be done in those who attended all the follow-up appointments (a compliant group), then a result in favour of Disulfiram was found. This is an *analysis with stratification by level of compliance.*

It is recommended that treatment studies attempt to measure compliance and present results both with and without stratification in terms of compliance.

F. Treatment withdrawals

A difficulty arises in knowing whether to include in the analysis the patients who do badly in the allocated treatment group and are withdrawn from the study. It would seem correct to leave them in the original group, perhaps allocating them an outcome score as at the point of withdrawal. Deaths should be divided into those deaths not attributed to alcohol (when patients should be excluded from the whole analysis) and deaths where alcohol or the treatment contributed, in which case they could be allocated an outcome score reflecting very poor outcome.

G. Length of Follow-up

There may be a rebound worsening after an effective treatment is terminated. This could occur in the case of a sedative drug that had a withdrawal syndrome associated with it, which a patient might treat by further drinking. Ideally, all treatment studies should include a post-treatment period of study.

The other important consideration touching on length of follow-up is the instability which has been demonstrated of 'short-term abstention'. This was a term used by Polich, Armour and Braiker (1980). It was found that individuals who had attained six months or fewer months of abstinence had a high likelihood of relapse in the next four years. Stable abstainers have usually attained at least twelve months abstinence. Nevertheless, as Tennant (1986) has emphasised, the cumulative effects of alcohol on health and wellbeing are such that even short periods of reduced drinking or abstinence should be striven for in patients with a chronic relapsing condition such as alcohol dependence.

REFERENCES

American Psychiatric Association (1989) *Diagnostic and Statistical Manual of Mental Disorders, 3rd edition revised (DSM-3-r)* Washington DC APA.

Andreasson, S., Parmander, M. and Allebreck, P. (1990) 'A trial that failed, and the reasons why: Comparing the Minnesota model with outpatient treatment and non-treatment for alcohol disorders', *Scandinavian Journal of Social Medicine* 18, 221–4.

Azrin, N.H., Sisson, R.W., Meyers, R. and Godley, M. (1982) 'Alcoholism treatment by disulfiram and community reinforcement therapy', *Journal of Behaviour Therapy and Experimental Psychiatry* 13, 105–12.

Babor, T.F., Staphens, R.S. and Marlatt, G.A. (1987) 'Verbal report methods in clinical research on alcoholism; response bias and its minimisation', *Journal of Studies on Alcohol* 48, 410–24.

Barrucand, R., Paille, F. and Gillet, C. (1987) 'Le syndrome subaigu de sevrage et son traitement chez le malade alcoolique', *Bulletin de la Société Française d'Alcoologie* Numéro Spécial, Sept., 17–26.

Bell, H. and Steensland, H. (1987) 'Serum activity of gamma glutamyl transpeptidase (GGT) in relation to estimated alcohol consumption and questionnaires in alcohol dependence syndrome', *British Journal of Addiction* 82, 1021–6.

Brown, S.A. and Schuckit, M.A. (1988) 'Changes in depression among abstinent alcoholics', *Journal of Studies on Alcohol* 49, 412–17.

Chaney, E.F., O'Leary, M.R. and Marlatt, G.A. (1978) 'Skills training with alcoholics', *Journal of Consulting and Clinical Psychology* 46, 1092–104.

Chick, J., Kreitman, N. and Plant, M.A. (1981) 'Mean cell volume and gamma glutamyl transpeptidase as markers of drinking in working men', *Lancet* i, 1249–51.

Chick, J., Lloyd, G. and Crombie, E. (1985) 'Counselling problem drinkers in medical wards: a controlled study', *British Medical Journal* 290, 965–7.

Chick, J., Ritson, E.B., Connaughton, J. et al. (1988) 'Advice versus extended treatment for alcoholism: a controlled study', *British Journal of Addiction* 83, 159–70.

Chick, J., Falkowski, W., Gough, K., Kershaw, P., Hore, B., Mehta, B., Ritson, B., Ropner, R., Torley, D. (in press) 'Supervised disulfiram in the treatment of alcoholism', *British Journal of Psychiatry*.

De Soto, C.B., O'Donnell, W.E., Allred, L.J. and Lupes, C.E. (1985) 'Symptomatology in alcoholics at various stages of abstinence', *Alcoholism (NY)* 9, 505–12.

Drummond, D.C., Thom, B., Brown, C., Edwards, G. and Mullan, M.J. (1990) 'Specialist versus general practitioner treatment of problem drinkers', *Lancet* 336, 915–19.

Edwards, G. (1989) 'As the years go rolling by: drinking problems in the time dimension', *British Journal of Psychiatry* 154, 18–26.

Emrick, C.D. (1975) 'A review of psychologically oriented treatment of alcoholism. II: the relative effectiveness of different treatment approaches and the relative effectiveness of treatment versus no treatment', *Journal of Studies on Alcohol* 36, 88–108.

Fawcett, J.C., Clark, D.C., Aagesen, C.A. et al. (1987) 'A double-blind placebo-controlled trial of lithium carbonate therapy for alcoholism', *Archives of General Psychiatry* 44, 248–56.

Fuller, R.K., Branchey, L., Brightwell, D.R. et al. (1986) 'Disulfiram treatment of alcoholism: a Veterans Administration cooperative study', *Journal of the American Medical Association* 256, 1449–55.

Gerrein, J.R., Rosenberg, C.M. and Manohar, V. (1973) 'Disulfiram maintenance in outpatient treatment of alcoholism', *Archives of General Psychiatry* 28, 798–802.

Hore, B. (1988) 'Advice versus extended treatment for alcoholism', Letter, *British Journal of Addiction* 83, p. 969.

Kadden, R.M., Cooney, N.L., Getter, H. and Litt, M.D. (1989) 'Matching alcoholics to coping skills or international therapies: post-treatment results', *Journal of Consulting and Clinical Psychology* 57, 698–704.

Keso, L. and Salaspuro, M. (1990) 'Comparative value of self-report and blood tests in assessing outcome among alcoholics', *British Journal of Addiction* 85, 209–16.

Kirstenson, H., Ohlin, H., Hulten-Nosslin, M.B., Trell, E., Hood, B. (1983) 'Identification and intervention of heavy drinking in middle-aged men: results and follow-up of 24–60 months of long-term study with randomised controls', *Alcoholism (NY)* 7, 203–9.

Latcham, R. (1986) 'Gamma glutamyl transpeptidase and mean cell volume: their usefulness in the assessment of inpatient alcoholics', *British Journal of Psychiatry* 149, 353–6.

Lhuintre, J.P., Moore, N., Tran, G. et al. (1990) 'Acamprosate appears to decrease alcohol intake in weaned alcoholics', *Alcohol and Alcoholism* 2–5, 613–22.

Liskow, B.I. and Goodwin, D.W. (1987) 'Pharmacological treatment of alcohol intoxication, withdrawal and dependence: a critical review', *Journal of Studies on Alcohol* 48, 356–70.

Lloyd, G., Chick, J. and Crombie, E. (1982) 'Screening for problem drinkers among medical in-patients', *Drug and Alcohol Dependence* 10, 355–9.

Mackenzie, A., Funderburk, F.R., Allen, R.P. and Stefan, R.L. (1987) 'The characteristics of alcoholics frequently lost to follow-up', *Journal of Studies of Alcohol* 48, 119–23.

Midanik, L.T. (1989) 'Validity of self-reported alcohol use: a literature review and assessment', *British Journal of Addiction* 83, 1019–29.

Miller, W.R. and Hester, R.K. (1986) 'The effectiveness of alcoholism treatment: What research reveals' in Miller, W.R. and Heather, N. (Eds), *Treating Addictive Behaviour: Processes of Change*, New York, Plenum, 121–74.

Miller, W.R. (1987) 'Behavioural alcohol treatment research advances: the barriers to utilisation', *Advances in Behaviour Research and Therapy* 9, 145–64.

Moos, R.H., Bliss, F. (1978) 'Difficulty of follow-up and outcome of alcoholism', *Journal of Studies on Alcohol* 39, 473–90.

Nordstrom, G., Berglund, M. (1987) 'A prospective study of successful long-term adjustment in alcohol dependence – social drinking versus abstinence', *Journal of Studies of Alcohol* 48, 95–103.

Polich, J.M., Armour, D.J. and Braiker, H.B. (1980) *The Course of Alcoholism: Four Years After Treatment*, Santa Monica, Rand Corporation.

Potamianos, G., North, W.R.S. and Peters, T.J. (1985) 'The relationship between daily ethanol consumption, haematological and hepatic indices of toxicity and severity of alcohol dependence in problem drinkers presenting at a district general hospital', *Alcohol and Alcoholism* 20, 387–90.

Shaw, G.K., Majumdar, S.K., Waller, S., MacGarvie, J. and Dunn, G. (1987) 'Tiapride in the long-term management of alcoholics of anxious or depressive temperament', *British Journal of Psychiatry* 150, 164–8.

Sinclair, J.D. (1987) 'The feasibility of effective psychopharmacological treatments for alcoholism', *British Journal of Addiction* 82, 1213–23.

Storey, E.L., Anderson, G.J., Mack, U., Powell, L.W. and Halliday, J.W. (1987) 'Desialylated transferrin as a serological marker of chronic excessive alcohol ingestion', *Lancet* i, 1292–4.

Tennant, F.S. (1986) 'Disulfiram will reduce medical complications but not cure alcoholism', *Journal of the American Medical Association* 256, 1489.

Vaillant, G.E. (1988) 'What can long-term follow-up teach us about relapse and prevention of relapse in addiction?' *British Journal of Addiction* 83, 1147–58.

World Health Organization (1978) *Mental Disorders: Glossary and Guide to Their Classification in Accordance with the 9th Revision of the International Classification of Diseases*, Geneva, World Health Organization.

22. Professional training

KEN BARRIE

'Training on drug misuse across a wide range of professions is vitally important to ensure that people are properly equipped to work efficiently and sensitively with problem drug users' (Michael Forsyth, Health Minister at Scottish Office 1990).

Despite equivocal evidence regarding the effectiveness of intervention or treatment for alcohol and drug problems, much has been written on the need for a better response from the helping professions. Cynics might suggest that any response at all from such professions would be a step in the right direction. This chapter will explore professional training on the basis of reports of statutory and professional bodies. Research findings on the impact of education and training provided for professional workers, both in the specialist and non-specialist setting, will be considered. Finally, developments in the field of alcohol and drug training will be outlined in conjunction with changes in the further and higher education spheres.

SOCIAL POLICY

The large increase in alcohol consumption in the United Kingdom in the 1960s and 1970s and the increase in illicit drug use in the 1980s resulted in changing views of problem drinkers and drug users. A shift away from viewing such individuals as suffering from an 'illness' or from psychiatric conditions implied that professionals other than those in the psychiatric field had a role to play. Similarly, the sheer numbers of problem drinkers/drug users requiring assistance from the social work and health services indicated that workers in such agencies required relevant education and training. Shaw et al. (1978) reported that problem drinkers sought generic services on a regular basis; that they were three times more likely to be referred on than other client groups; and that professionals involved felt threatened on the basis of lack of knowledge, support and clarity as to whether they should respond to problem drinkers. The (English and Welsh) Advisory Council on Alcoholism (1978, 1979) envisaged professional workers at the primary level caring for the majority of problem drinkers, supported by secondary level workers who would also have responsibility for the more difficult cases. It is also stated that 'all should have a responsibility for prevention' (Advisory Council on Alcoholism 1979, p. 4).

The Advisory Council on the Misuse of Drugs (ACMD) (1982, 1990) indicated the need for training on an 'integrated' basis, i.e. including all substances despite having a remit which excludes alcohol, solvents and tobacco. Despite the broadly welcomed reports by the ACMD (1982, 1984, 1988, 1989, 1990), it is over a decade since any governmental body has commented in detail on the need for training to improve service responses for problem drinkers.

The ACMD (1990) recommendations for training are aimed at four target areas: professional training, post-qualifying, and specialist and non-specialist workers. In all instances, advisory bodies' recommendations are subject to filtering through employers and professional bodies whose aims and objectives tend to have given alcohol and drug problems scant attention.

The ACMD (1990) suggests general aims across the professions, thus going further than the simple identification and training of specialist workers. Beyond specialism, it is suggested that training at an advanced level be provided for key resource staff and that all staff should have a basic understanding and awareness of drug-related problems. To this end, professional validation bodies are advised to give 'priority to determining the basic levels of drug related knowledge skills and understanding appropriate to their profession' (p. 21). That this is recommended as a priority is perhaps a measure of the lack of movement on this matter in the preceding two decades. The Scottish Council on Alcohol (1984) noted the limited attention given to enable social work students to recognise alcohol-related problems and apply appropriate transferable counselling skills to the situation. The Central Council for Education and Training in Social Work (CCETSW) (1987) acknowledged this type of critique with regard to failure to include adequate coverage of drug, alcohol and substance misuse. With regard to the medical profession, it has been noted that: 'On the subject of drug misuse doctors have long been saying that they receive no real training as medical students and that post graduate training is also conspicuous by its absence' (Banks and Waller, 1988, p. 281).

Despite this comment, the topic of alcohol and drug use is in competition on most professional courses, whether social work, nursing or medical, with the needs of other client/patient groups. Professional bodies and employing agencies while having made training responses in respect of HIV/AIDS, have done little to advance and develop training on drug- and alcohol-related problems in a wider context.

NON-SPECIALIST WORKERS

Non-specialist professional workers' responses to alcohol problems have long been a source of concern. Shaw et al. (1978) found that respondents in an English general population survey who drank heavily and had problems were three times more likely than other people to have contact with primary care workers (e.g. social workers, GPs, health visitors etc.), though none of them were receiving any help specifically for their drinking problems. Shaw et al. suggested three main factors underlying primary care workers' inadequate response:

(1)   Role adequacy: the perception that one has the knowledge and skills to work with problem drinkers and drug users.

(2)   Role legitimacy: the perception that working with problem drinkers and drug users is part of the professional task.

(3)   Role support: having someone within the organization who would provide support, advice and guidance.

Workers experiencing an insufficiency in all three interacting aspects of the model were considered 'role-insecure'. The effect of this might even suggest active avoidance of dealing with the alcohol or drug components of an individual's set of problems. Barrie (1982) supported the conclusions of Shaw et al. with regard to alcohol problems. He concluded that social workers experienced even greater 'role insecurity' with regard to problem drug use. The concept of the Community Alcohol Team (CAT) was developed with the primary aim of reducing role insecurity by providing education and training and a consultation service, thereby altering the three factors identified as barriers to providing effective responses. Such research was taken as the green light for training on alcohol and drug problems, whereby the educational input would increase role adequacy and legitimacy, and consultation would provide role support by an 'outside' specialist in the absence of such support being available from managers or colleagues within the organization, be it health or social care. McKenna (1987), evaluating the Renfrew Community Alcohol Team, demonstrated that health and social work professionals felt more confident about their knowledge skills and efforts when working with problem drinkers, subsequent to a multidisciplinary training event of eighteen hours' duration. However, workers remained indifferent to working with problem drinkers. The issue then became how to improve 'role support' either from an external agency or from within the primary care agency.

Clement (1987), reporting on the Salford Community Alcohol Team, suggests that the provision of role support has to come first and foremost from managers of primary care workers before external consultants are used. Lightfoot and Orford (1986), elaborating on the Shaw et al. (1978) model, identified differences between community psychiatric nurses and social workers in their receptiveness to training on alcohol-related problems. Situational constraints such as time, policy, encouragement and level of priority indicated that social workers were much more limited by statutory and organizational demands than were community psychiatric nurses. These constraints made it harder for them to benefit from training events and less likely to develop role supports. It seems reasonable to expect that, under such 'constrained' conditions, training would have only a very limited impact on workers, whereby any skills learned are not supported and encouraged on return to the working environment. In this context, the effectiveness of training is strongly influenced by the needs and requirements of the employing organization rather than the personal attributes of the training course participants. For the highly 'constrained' worker, amelioration of the situation is unlikely to result from training but rather from alteration of resource and time allocation, policy and priorities.

SPECIALIST WORKERS

Specialist workers in the drug and alcohol field come from a wide range of backgrounds. These include those from professional helping occupations who have opted to work in specialised settings in the statutory and non-statutory services and those who have no experience in the helping fields but who have a commitment to helping those with alcohol and drug problems. Consequently, the training and educational needs of such a range of workers is very varied. Those from an established professional background may need to identify existing professional skills and apply them in the specialist setting as well as develop specific knowledge about drug and alcohol problems, including HIV/AIDS. By contrast, the non-professionally qualified workers, many of whom are unpaid volunteers, have to develop an adequate knowledge base as well as acquire a range of skills to enable them to work effectively with problem drinkers and drug users. The training available to this group, usually on an in-service basis, is effectively their professional qualification and is provided by the Scottish Drugs Training Project at the University of Stirling. In addition to in-service training, the Alcohol Studies Centre at Paisley College offers a full-time postgraduate course on alcohol and drug problems which has academic and professional (nursing and social work) approval and is open to those from the voluntary field.

Educational and vocational development

Regardless of changes within the field of alcohol and drugs training, there have been substantial developments within the vocational and education field. While the Advisory Council on the Misuse of Drugs

(1990) has made recommendations to all professional groups with regard to drugs training, and by implication 'alcohol' training, the educational sphere has developed a flexibility which might facilitate access to those wishing to develop vocational qualifications relevant to alcohol and drugs problems whether in the specialist or non-specialist setting.

Credit Accumulation Transfer Schemes have been pioneered by the Council for National Academic Awards (CNAA) at the higher education level. This scheme allows students a much wider range of choice in the types of courses which they may undertake. It effectively allows them to build their own educational experiences and qualifications at appropriate levels. The scheme has been adopted by the Central Council for Education and Training in Social Work (CCETSW) as the basis upon which professional social work qualifying training and post-qualifying training will be based. It is likely that the nursing profession will move to incorporate a variant of this scheme as a basis for nurse education and training in the future. Credit Accumulation Transfer Schemes may offer educational institutions and professional bodies the opportunity to develop academically approved and professionally validated courses at levels appropriate to the needs of a wide range of workers in the alcohol and drugs field.

Central issues

Making training work

While education and training are highly-prized activities in Scottish culture, the evidence supporting its effectiveness is limited (Clement 1986; McKenna 1987; Lightfoot and Orford 1986). This research evidence points to policy and other constraints within the organization which militate against effective work with problem drinkers and drug users who already form part of the workload. It may be that a logical response to this would be to target education and training not exclusively at front-line primary care workers but at middle and senior managers, who are in a position to influence and alter the policy and practice.

Alcohol and illicit drugs

Although there is widespread acceptance of the notion of 'integrated' training encompassing all substances and of the similarities in addictive behaviour regardless of the substance involved, the world of service delivery and practice can be rather different. Alcohol and drugs are dealt with by different parts of the Scottish and indeed UK government machinery. Consequently, the availability of funding and funding arrangements vary to the extent that some agencies have limitations as to the substance problems to which they can respond. These are not simply educational or training matters but are issues which reflect our culture's view of responses to alcohol-and drug-related problems. Again reflecting cultural factors, the 1980s have seen a large increase in concern and training about drug-related issues, referred to as a 'moral panic' by some. Yet despite alcohol consumption and problems being nearly as high as they have ever been in the previous four decades, there has been little alteration in concern or increase in resources for either training or service delivery.

HIV/AIDS

The spread of HIV/AIDS in Scotland has been discussed earlier in this book. This has had a major impact on the pre-existing specialist drug agencies which have become a major part of the AIDS prevention strategy and, by implication on their training and educational requirements. This has happened with little increase in the resources allocated to training organizations. Consequently, it is possible that drug education is being diluted by the need to provide an HIV/AIDS dimension within the same limited resources and time allocation. This in turn may make some drug services less responsive to the many problem drug users who are not at risk, at least on the basis of their drug use, of developing HIV. This should not detract from the need to provide education and training as a means of preventing HIV. Even so, it should be emphasised that HIV is not only associated with intravenous drug use.

Evaluation

While there is a literature focusing on attempts to influence the responses of the primary care workers, particularly toward alcohol-related problems (Shaw et al. 1978; Clement 1987), it is not extensive. Besides this, there has been very little published on training professional workers either at professional qualifying or post-qualifying levels. Consequently, it is not known to any degree of exactness what training inputs will be effective, for whom they will be effective and under what circumstances they will have a positive impact. Similarly, given the wide-ranging backgrounds of workers, specialist alcohol and drug agencies', evaluation of the impact of training would be very difficult. Part of the problem may be a reluctance on behalf of training providers to evaluate their own work or to allow independent research to be carried out.

CONCLUSION

There is a considerable need and demand for professional training, whether in the specialist or non-specialist setting. That demand, however, may still be masked by employers' and professional organizations' inability or reluctance to identify the extent to which alcohol and drug problems have an impact on their primary functions. It is also clear that training is less likely to be effective without the expressed approval and interest of professional and employing organizations:

> Training by itself, though, is not a panacea; it cannot operate in isolation or provide magical answers. It can only be effective if services are adequately funded to enable staff to offer high-quality care and support to clients and to the community (Cranfield and Dixon 1990, p. 195).

The potential to develop professionally validated and relevant education may be facilitated by more flexibility in the further and higher education sphere. It is less clear, however, where the resources in financial and other terms will come from.

REFERENCES

Advisory Council on Alcoholism (1978) *The Pattern and Range of Services*, Department of Health and Social Security, London.
Advisory Council on Alcoholism (1979) *Report on Training and Education for Professional Staff and Voluntary Workers in the Field*, Department of Health and Social Security and Welsh Office, London.
Advisory Council on the Misuse of Drugs (1982) *Treatment and Rehabilitation*, HMSO, London.
Advisory Council on the Misuse of Drugs (1984) *Prevention*, Home Office, HMSO, London.
Advisory Council on the Misuse of Drugs (1988) *AIDS and Drug Misuse: Part 1*, Home Office, HMSO, London.
Advisory Council on the Misuse of Drugs (1989) *AIDS and Drug Misuse: Part 2*, Home Office, HMSO, London.
Advisory Council on the Misuse of Drugs (1990) *Problem Drug Use: A Review of Training*, Home Office, HMSO, London.
Banks, A. and Waller, T.A.N. (1988) *Drug Misuse: A Practical Handbook for General Practitioners*, Blackwell Scientific, Oxford.
Barrie, K. (1982) *Social Workers' Attitudes Towards Working with Problem Drinkers and Drug Takers*, unpublished report. Alcohol Studies Centre, Paisley College, Paisley.
Central Council for Education and Training in Social Work (1987) *Statement of Minimum Requirements of the Social Worker on the Point of Qualification*. Central Council for Education and Training in Social Work, London.
Clements, S. (1987) 'The Salford Experiment: an account of the Community Alcohol Team approach', in Stockwell, T. and Clements, R. (Eds), *Helping the Problem Drinkers. New Initiatives in Community Care*, London, Groom, 121–44.
Collins, S., Ottley, G. and Wilson, M. (1988) 'Counselling problem drinkers and social work education in Scotland', *Social Work Education* vol. 7, no. 3, 17–23.
Forsyth, M. (1990) *Scottish Office News Release*, Scottish Information Office, Edinburgh.
Lightfoot, P. and Orford, J. (1986) 'Helping agents' attitudes towards alcohol-related problems; situations vacant? A test and elaboration of a model', *British Journal of Addiction*, 81, 749–56.
McKenna, S. (1987) *Evaluation of Community Alcohol Team Impact Upon Primary Care Workers' Attitudes Toward Working with Problem Drinkers*, Renfrew Community Alcohol Team, Paisley.
Scottish Council on Alcohol (1984) *Survey of Alcohol Education on CQSW/CSS Courses*, SCA, Glasgow.
Shaw, S., Cartwright, A., Spratley, T. and Harwin, J. (1978) *Responding to Drinking Problems*, Croom Helm, London.

Name index

Subject index

Aberdeen 106, 147–9
acetaldehyde 19
AIDS *see* HIV/AIDS
Albyn House 147–9
alcohol:
  and adolesents 67-8; *see also* education
    alcohol advertising and young people
      83–7
    appreciation 86–7
    awareness 86–8
    imagery 84–5
    Scottish research 84–7
  and cancer 19
  and drug education *see* education
  and increased risk of HIV/AIDS 19
  and pregnancy *see* fetal alcohol
    syndrome
  and public health 23–4
  and public order problems 18
  and social policy 181–2
  and tissue damage 18–9
  and young offenders 104–9; *see also*
    young offenders
  associated accidents and injuries 21–2
  benefits to health 23
  consumption and econometric studies
    82–3
  history of in Scotland *see* Scottish
    drinking culture
  in Scottish prisons 163–4
  markets for alcohol 82
  patterns of consumption in Scotland 20
  per capita consumption in the United
    Kingdom 4
  related problems 4
  services in Scotland 123–6, 131–6
  sex workers and alcohol consumption
    36–7
  unit of alcohol 23–4
Alcoholics Anonymous 123, 131
alimentary disorders 21
ambivalence 18
assessing impact of alcohol upon health
  20–2

atrophy 19 *see also* brain damage

benzodiazepines 168
birth defects and heavy drinking 27; *see
  also* Fetal Alcohol Syndrome
brain damage 19
breath testing 99–102; *see also* drinking
  and driving

cancer and alcohol 19
cannabis 166–7
cigarette smoking *see* tobacco
cirrhosis 19, 22, 94; *see also* liver
community-based drug agencies 139
  involvement in prison drug misuse 169
community care 153
Community Care Act (1990) 144
Community Drug Problem Service 140–2
  aims 140–1
  effects 142
  referrals 141
condom use 36–8
coronary (ischaemic) heart disease 23

detoxification 156
dideoxyinosine (DDI) 160
disinhibition 34
drinking and driving:
  and problem drinkers 101–2
  effect of 1976 Licensing (Scotland) Act
    94–5
  high risk offenders 102
  Random Breath Testing 99–102
  Road Traffic Act 1967 98
  Road Traffic Law Reform Bill 102
  statistics 99
drinking, binge 21
drinking habits in the United Kingdom
  3–5
drugs *see* illicit drugs *and* psychoactive
  drugs
Dumbarton 106
Dundee 44, 49, 104–5, 123, 127, 139–40
Dutch courage 34